A View from the Hill

A Blewbury Village Society Publication
by the Local Environment Group

Edited by Peter Cockrell and Shirley Kay

PUBLISHED BY THE BLEWBURY VILLAGE SOCIETY 2006
COPYRIGHT © PETER COCKRELL

ISBN-10: 0-955 3992-0-3
ISBN-13: 978-0-955 3992-0-6

Chalk Hill Blue
Painting by Richard Lewington

Contents

ACKNOWLEDGEMENTS

The editors, authors and publishers are grateful to all those who have contributed in any way to the preparation of this book; we have been overwhelmed by the enthusiastic response we have received. Individual contributions are gratefully acknowledged in each chapter but particular gratitude is also extended to the following who have made important general contributions to the work.

Archaeological advice – Paul Smith
Presentation advice, book-title, and map-work – Elphin Lloyd-Jones
Commissioned, historical illustrations – Richard Hook of Linden Artists
Paintings and drawings – Joan Durbin, Ron Freeborn,
Ian Lewington, Richard Lewington, and Marion Whiting
Special photography and general support – Bernard Mattimore
Book design and pre-press – Loraine Fergusson
Aerial Pictures – taken by the Photographic Section, RAF Benson
Proof reading – Norma Bird, Richard Bird, José Cockrell, Mike Marshall, Hugh Osborn,
Bernardine Shirley-Smith, Grant Tuff and Chris Whatmore
Studio lighting equipment – Colin Vinten
Website creation – Derek Marshall, Mike Marshall
and Bernardine Shirley-Smith
Copyright advice – Ian Wishart
Accounting and distribution – Tony Salter
Publicity advice – Charlotte Carey
Mapping advice – John Richards

The vital support of the following is also gratefully recognised:
Anthony and Carol Allen, the owners of Blewburton Hill
The representatives of English Heritage and BBOWT notably Richard Massey of English Heritage
and Camilla Lambrick of BBOWT.

The help of the BVS Environment Group who have hosted the project and provided both practical and moral support throughout is also gratefully acknowledged. The group members are, currently, (in alphabetical order): Norma Bird, Peter Cockrell, Mike Edmunds (Chair), Mike Marshall, Hugh Osborn, Anita Rendel, Bernardine Shirley-Smith, Joanna Thomson
and Grant Tuff.

Funded under The Local Heritage Initiative Scheme by The Heritage Lottery Fund
and made possible by the goodwill, knowledge and talent of everyone involved. Profits will be used to preserve and improve the local environment for wildlife, the community and visitors.

PROLOGUE: A VIEW OF BLEWBURTON HILL

The old coach road from the Midlands to Oxford traversed a succession of geological zones from the Triassic rocks of the Midland Plain to newer formations of alternate bands of low clay vales and oolite limestone uplands. There were steep hills where the road zig-zagged up the scarp slopes, and long straight stretches where the underlying rocks dipped gently to the south. At the top of Dane Hill, south of Deddington, one could see an unmistakable landmark, two clumps of trees crowning two hills, the Sinodun Hills or Wittenham Clumps. Once part of the long line of Berkshire Downs to their south, they had, through long ages of erosion, become separated from the main chalk body, and were now "outliers". Of similar detached formation, though without a crown of beech trees, is Blewburton Hill which overlooks the spreading arable fields around it.

These chalk outliers were natural "islands" rising above the forested and marshy claylands, and so they attracted early settlements. Iron Age homes on Castle Hill, Wittenham, were protected by a deep ditch and rampart, while on Blewburton Hill a defensive steep scarp and ditch were constructed. Below this, four cultivation terraces or lynchets were made later, probably in medieval times, on the west side of the hill.

During the centuries Blewburton has seen Roman occupation, Saxon, Danish and Norman invasions have brought changing scenes to the locality. From Wittenham Clumps in the 18th Century, one might have looked across the Dyke Hills towards Wallingford, where Jethro Tull was perfecting his seed drill and his horse hoe - pioneering the agrarian revolution. The smoke and steam from Brunel's Great Western Railway, viewed from Blewburton, heralded a new era of swifter travel, and in more recent times the horse-drawn self-binder disappeared from the harvest scene to be succeeded by the tractor and the combine harvester.

The hill, aloof from such agricultural activity, has been a haven for wildlife, wild flowers and birds. Blewburton Hill is a lowly eminence but despite its relatively modest altitude, its value as an unchanging feature in a changing environment, and a means of enjoying the Oxfordshire landscape, is immeasurable.

WILLIAM DENT-ROBINSON, BLEWBURY 2005

WILLIAM DENT-ROBINSON AND HIS WIFE WINIFRED WERE TEACHERS IN THE AREA FROM 1930 TO 1973. FROM 1943 TO 1946 WILLIAM SERVED IN A FRONTLINE RAF WIRELESS INTELLIGENCE UNIT TAKING PART IN THE NORMANDY LANDINGS AND THE ENSUING EUROPEAN CAMPAIGN.

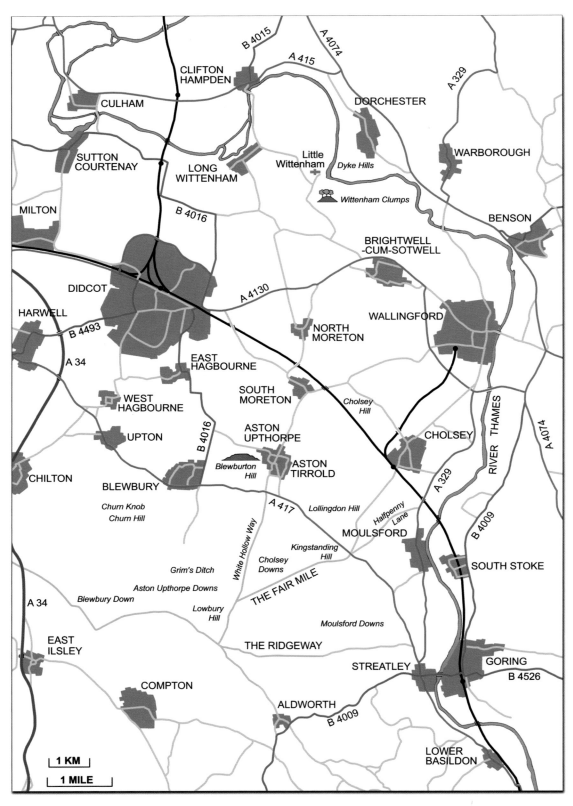

THE WORK OF ELPHIN LLOYD-JONES IN CREATING THE MAP IN THIS ARTICLE IS GRATEFULLY ACKNOWLEDGED.
SOME INFORMATION ON THE MAP WAS REPRODUCED BY PERMISSION OF ORDNANCE SURVEY ON BEHALF OF HMSO.

PART I
A FAVOURED ENVIRONMENT

RON FREEBORN

The Quiet Hill
*No habitation since Saxon
Times, no ghosts, a place for quiet
contemplation. Blewburton Hill
with Wittenham Clumps and
Brightwell Barrow beyond.*

OUTSTANDING NATURAL BEAUTY

Sitting on top of Blewburton Hill contemplating the lives of the people who created the distinctive ditches and terraces of the hill fort, it is easy to imagine why they chose to live here, close to the spring line, between the chalk escarpment to the south, and the fertile flood plain to the north. The area is now part of the North Wessex Downs Area of Outstanding Natural Beauty with the same importance as a national park. It was designated an AONB in 1972 to conserve and enhance its special qualities and to promote sustainable development and enjoyment of the area.

The Hill is located on the north-eastern corner of the North Wessex Downs. In the distance to the east, the Chilterns continue the line of chalk through to Ivinghoe Beacon. To the west across the Vale of White Horse, the Golden Ridge of Faringdon is clearly visible, and in the far distance you may see the hazy outline of the Cotswolds. The Hill enjoys three different landscape characters all within one sweeping gaze from the hilltop: Blewbury Downs, Moreton Plain and the Thames Valley Floodplain.

THE DOWNS

To the south lies the rolling open downland of Blewbury Downs, a chalk-based landscape with a distinct, steep and deeply convoluted scarp slope rising above Blewbury village. Churn Knob is clearly visible on the skyline, reminding us of the place where St Birinus preached his first Christian sermon. Over the top and out of sight are the villages of Compton, West Ilsley and East Ilsley in dry river valleys carved out of the chalk. The great mass of chalk itself is composed of the myriad fossils of miniscule sea creatures which lived in a warm sea 100 million years ago. The thin layer of soil over the chalk on Blewbury Downs sustains farming, racehorse training and thousands of visitors who, every year, walk, cycle and ride the network of footpaths and byways. The Ridgeway National Trail is easy to reach from here. The steep scarp slopes also provide perfect unimproved habitats for flower-rich chalk grassland. There are four Sites of Special Scientific Interest on the eastern edge of the

(Top): Scorpion Fly; Bloody Nose Beetle; Lesser Stag Beetle; Soldier Beetle; and Common Snail.

Blewbury Downs. Lardon Chase is one of the largest remaining fragments of unimproved chalk grassland; the rare Adonis Blue butterfly can be found here. Aston Upthorpe Downs is another perfect habitat for a wide variety of butterflies. Moulsford Downs supports unusual insects such as juniper shield bug and several beetle species. At Streatley Warren you will find birds including willow warbler, lesser whitethroat,

The rare Adonis Blue butterfly

blackcap and yellowhammer taking advantage of the native shrubs and trees, including juniper in one of the few places where this evergreen shrub occurs naturally. The wonderfully rich biodiversity of this landscape is explored in detail later in the book.

MORETON PLAIN

Turning north towards the twin outcrops of Wittenham Clumps atop Sinodun Hills and the lone tree on Brightwell Barrow your gaze sweeps across the landscape of the Moreton Plain. This is a landscape with a varied geology of chalk and greensand giving a chalky flinty soil with the outcrops of Cholsey and Sinodun hills; geological sisters to Blewburton Hill itself. The medieval field patterns and sinuous hedges between Little and Long Wittenham are in marked contrast with the regular fenced paddocks of Aston Upthorpe Stud. These show the changes in land use over the centuries from simple, prehistoric farming, to the multi-million dollar business of breeding racehorses today.

Autumn Gentian growing on almost pure chalk.

THE THAMES VALLEY

Just east of Aston Upthorpe village is the third landscape character: the Thames Valley Floodplain. The River Thames becomes the eastern boundary of the North Wessex Downs AONB at Cholsey and runs south to Purley-on-Thames. Numerous watercourses and streams such

The River Thames near Goring, entrance to the North Wessex Downs AONB.

as The Mill Brook, all flowing to the Thames, cross the Moreton area of the Thames Valley Floodplain. The land has been drained to make it suitable for agriculture. In the spring this gives a spectacular mosaic effect of verdant green young crops next to sparkling yellow rape, and in the autumn, the rich shades of brown ploughed earth. Few roads cross this low-lying landscape, and in spite of the pylons and power lines from Didcot, the area retains its remote and isolated character.

MANMADE LANDSCAPE

The North Wessex Downs we see today is a man-made landscape. Over the millennia man has worked with the constraints of the landform and geology to exploit opportunities for settlement, agriculture and trade. The second part of this book is about the ancient and medieval history of this area, who settled here and why, who traded on the tracks between the river and the downland. The landscape is rich in evidence of people in times past: local names, place names, old buildings, boundaries ancient roadways, dropped coins, hidden jewellery, and buried weapons.

Racehorses on the gallops.

WHAT WILL THE VIEW FROM THE HILL BE IN THE FUTURE?

The beauty, tranquillity and special qualities of the landscape will continue to be conserved and enhanced by the local authorities, land owners, farmers, utilities, conservation groups and others who care for the North Wessex Downs, for the enjoyment of everyone. Writing in the foreword to the AONB Management Plan, Martin Spray, then chairman of the Council of Partners and Director of Berkshire, Buckinghamshire and Oxfordshire Wildlife Trust wrote:

Brown Trout and a Grayling from the pure water of a downland chalkstream.

© PETER COCKERELL

   With their chalk rivers and streams, woodlands and copses, picturesque villages and towns, and ancient archaeological heritage, the North Wessex Downs provide a welcome serenity for all who live, work or visit in an increasingly busy and pressured southern England.

   The Management Plan is for everyone who values the area. A wide variety of organisations and many individuals from across the AONB contributed to it, and now deliver its actions. The Actions cover: local character, landscape as inspiration to the arts, new types of farming, community-led renewable energy schemes, planning, the development of urban fringe action plans, and green infrastructure planning to link towns with the landscape.

   The Plan establishes a sound framework for organisations and local people to work together for the benefit of the North Wessex Downs AONB and its local communities. It has created a shared purpose and direction so that everyone can play a part in conserving and enhancing the landscape for future generations to enjoy their View from the Hill.

WENDY TOBITT, NORTH WESSEX DOWNS AONB

PERMISSION TO USE THE ADONIS BLUE BUTTERFLY PHOTOGRAPH BY JIM ASHER, IS ALSO GRATEFULLY ACKNOWLEDGED. (SEE ALSO THE ARTICLE ON DOWN LAND BUTTERFLIES)
THANKS ARE ALSO DUE TO GERARD BUTLER OF CHURN STABLES FOR HELP WITH THE DOWNLAND PICTURE WITH HORSES AND RIDERS.

GEOLOGY AND WATER RESOURCES

THE GEOLOGICAL COLUMN WAS DEVISED BY PROFESSOR EDMUNDS, FROM MATERIAL SUPPLIED BY THE BRITISH GEOLOGICAL SURVEY, AND DRAWN BY GILL TYSON.

WHY IS THE HILL THERE?

Blewburton Hill owes its existence to a history involving warm tropical seas, great river deltas and semi-arid climates, ripples of the Alpine earth movements and finally a series of glaciations. The landscape seen today is little more than ten thousand years old. In early civilizations people moved mainly along the Thames Valley and may only have set foot on Blewburton Hill after the end of the Devensian glaciation around twelve thousand years ago. Why is the hill there and what was the importance of water in maintaining settlement of the hill and surrounding areas?

THE GEOLOGICAL HISTORY OF THE HILL

The foundations of Blewburton Hill are known from a borehole drilled just off the Aston-South Moreton road to search for coal in the 1980s. Diagram 1 shows that this borehole reached a depth of 750 metres and at its base identified red desert sandstones of Devonian age (some 380 million years old). Above this were laid down some 300 metres of Carboniferous rocks (shelly limestones and silty mudstones and sandstone – but no coal deposits!). These older rocks beneath Blewburton Hill were folded by the Variscan earth movements about 300 million years ago and after this remained a stable basement to our area – part of a platform of rocks extending eastwards to London and the continent – called the London Platform. These older rocks are only about 400 metres beneath Blewburton (about the same distance as the width of the village).

This old surface was then gradually submerged and a sequence of Jurassic limestones and clays (as found in the Cotswolds) was deposited. About 145 million years ago, the chalk, the main rock type forming Blewburton Hill and its neighbourhood began to be laid down. The Chalk sequence was formed in a shallow tropical sea (rather like the Bahamas) and the sedimentation was only completed around 65 million years ago. By then, this was again part of a coastal region but covered by Tertiary sands, clays and muds produced in a semi-arid but tropical climate. Blewburton Hill and the neighbouring Chilterns were

Diagram 1: The rock layers from a borehole drilled near Aston Upthorpe when exploring for coal in the 1980s.

under water – but about this time another major event occurred – the formation of the Alps.

The south of England was strongly affected by the same forces that created the Alps and the gently rolling landscape of Wessex was the result. Blewbury and the Chilterns were on the northern limb of a large structure - the London Basin - whose rocks tilted gently towards the south. Without this structure there would be no Blewbury, no Blewburton Hill, since this gentle tilting led to the escarpment beneath which the villages of Blewbury and the Astons lie and which allow the springs to emerge where they are.

Over the next millennia the overlying rocks were slowly eroded by the action of rivers and chemical weathering, exposing the Chalk but leaving behind traces of harder covering rocks as sarsens (silicified soil deposits called silcretes, which were strongly resistant to erosion).

Today's landscape is strongly influenced by at least two Pleistocene glaciations. Although the ice caps never came further south than Aylesbury, Blewbury and its area were affected for thousands of years by frozen ground (permafrost). The renewed freezing and thawing helped to fracture the surface rocks and assist weathering of the Chalk.

Plate 1
Microphotograph of chalk showing the fossil remains of coccoliths with diameters of about a micron (one-thousandth of a millimetre).

THE CHALK

Blewburton Hill is made up entirely of chalk, formed in a shallow tropical sea. Although it gives the impression of being a sticky clay it is composed overwhelmingly of billions of minute fossils – plankton or, strictly, coccoliths – with diameters of about one micron (one thousandth of a millimeter). These microfossils have a distinctive cartwheel shape, made up of calcite (calcium carbonate) platelets [Plate 1]. It is surprising, perhaps, that even after so much time these small fossils are still largely intact. Because of their shape, the chalk sediment, when compacted on the sea bottom, remained significantly porous. Some clay minerals and larger fossils such as shells and sea-urchins are also found occasionally [Plate 2]

 Although the chalk is generally a soft rock, a number of "hard-grounds" occur. These developed when the shallow seas, in which the chalk formed, gave way to land. The carbonate minerals and fossils dissolved and re-precipitated under the influence of rainwater. Such

Plate 2
A fossil ammonite 15cms in diameter from the Lower Chalk in Blewbury.

hard-grounds are common in the Chalk and their frequency tells us how often the land emerged from the sea. Blewburton Hill owes its existence mainly to the protection of a capping of chalk hard-ground called the Melbourn Rock. This was used for rather poor quality building stone in Blewbury, where it was quarried from the Chalk Pit. In fact, the walk up to the Chalk Pit reveals a number of other harder bands or hard-grounds, including the Totternhoe Stone, also used in the Chilterns for building.

The Chalk found on Blewburton Hill is known as Lower Chalk, the top of which is marked by the Melbourn Rock. The Lower Chalk is rather impure and contains more clay than the overlying chalk layers. Above the Melbourn Rock are the Middle and Upper Chalks, which form the higher levels seen for example on the Ridgeway. Flints are common in the Middle and Upper Chalks, but they are absent from the Lower Chalk and hence from Blewburton Hill. Yet occasional flints may remain from the weathering out of overlying layers. These flints were formed as the chalk compacted on the sea bed and represent the decay products of the silica skeletons of sponges and other organisms. The flints were prized by early settlers; tools made from flint have been found in the area. Later on, flint was used as building stone for Blewbury church and other buildings.

How the Hill Took Shape

Blewburton Hill is an outlier of Lower Chalk, separated from the rest of its stratum by the A417. Its isolation is the result of natural weathering, perhaps helped by joints or east-west fractures in the Chalk aiding the erosion of the intervening ground. Most certainly the impact of nearby glaciers in the late Pleistocene and Devensian periods have shaped the landscape we see today. Constant freezing, thawing and possibly river action have eroded the rounded hill slopes, carrying debris downhill to form thick and fertile soils (as found on Blewburton's fields and allotments). The role of water in shaping the Blewbury landscape can also be seen clearly on the rounded nearby slopes of Lids Bottom (the name coming perhaps from the Anglo-Saxon "hlid" meaning "sloping ground"). The glacial climate finally receded about eleven thousand years ago, allowing the present soils and landscape to evolve as we see them today.

WATER RESOURCES AROUND BLEWBURTON HILL

The Chalk is the major aquifer of the Berkshire Downs as well as for the UK. Although it is porous, the very small size of the pores allows water to be stored but does not easily allow water to flow. Water movement takes place mainly through a complex fracture network, which is more extensive near the surface. The Lower Chalk of Blewbury and Blewburton, being richer in clay especially near its base, gives rise to the series of springs in the Astons and Blewbury. The nearest springs in Watts Lane and Aston Upthorpe were probably the sources of water for the settlers of fortified Blewburton Hill.

The springs are fed by rainfall (present day around 70 centimetres per year) on downland to the south. Some of this water evaporates but around 30% infiltrates into the Chalk, percolating at an average rate of about one metre per year to the water table. It has been shown that rain water may take up to fifty years to reach the springs. Under natural conditions, it is likely that over the recent millennia the major springs (and streams) around Blewburton would have been perennial and maintained a continuous supply.

Besides Blewburton, early settlement for over four thousand years is recorded in Blewbury where favoured sites were on higher ground around the Ash Brook. Although springs were relied upon, it is likely that shallow wells (often bell-shaped) were also dug from about five hundred years ago. By the nineteenth century most houses possessed a dug well conveniently situated adjacent to the house.

In 1935 an exploration borehole was sunk at Lids bottom, 500

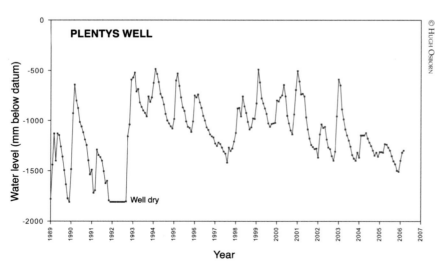

Diagram 2
The variations in water level from a well in Blewbury over the past seventeen years. The abnormal lowering of the water tables before 1993 was linked to excessive pumping from the Chalk and Greensand aquifers.

© Bernard Mattimore

Plate 3
Part of The Cleve, the watery
centre of Blewbury, which dried
out in 1992.

metres due south of Blewbury, to investigate the possibility of a public supply. This programme was interrupted by the war; further drilling and testing continued in 1947 and village supplies were established by 1951. The main borehole was drilled to 66 metres and reached the Gault Clay, overlain by Upper Greensand and Lower Chalk. For the last half of the 20th century, therefore, the village has been supplied by a blend of water from the Greensand and the Chalk, maintained by the higher water table of the Downs.

The flow in the village springs is known to have decreased with the start of pumping, since there is hydraulic connection between the boreholes and the village springs. Some reduction in flow was initially accepted as the price to pay for a mains water supply. However, the abstraction of water from the boreholes has steadily increased and water was exported to supply nearby villages. Diagram 2 shows the variations in water level from a well in Blewbury over the past seventeen years.

During the severe drought of 1976 the springs and some streams became dry. This trend continued during the dry winter of 1989 and especially in 1992 with an exceptionally dry winter. Concern was expressed at the loss of amenity, especially the drying of The Cleve [Plate 3], in conjunction with many other Chalk downland villages. The abnormal lowering of the water tables was linked to excessive pumping from the Chalk and Greensand aquifers, preventing sufficient flow to maintain the watercourses. Blewbury Pumping station has now closed so there may soon be a return to the hydrological conditions experienced by the early inhabitants of Blewburton.

PROFESSOR W. MIKE EDMUNDS

THE WATER LEVEL DATA WAS COLLECTED AND PRESENTED FOR THIS ARTICLE BY HUGH OSBORN.

FARMING TODAY AND YESTERDAY

The Allen family bought Blewburton Hill in 1957. At that time it formed part of Blewbury Barn Farm, which amounted to two hundred and fifty acres and ran from the Aston Road across the A417 to the Downs. It was owned by the Wade Estate based at Upthorpe Farm, Aston Tirrold. It then became part of Winterbrook Farm, which was purchased in 1951 and then totalled a hundred and fifty acres.

The previous owner of Winterbrook Farm was Mr Morny Higgs who built a range of farm buildings for farming wheat, potatoes and pigs. The only remaining old building at Winterbrook Farm is the white building as you enter the yard, which was the mill house for milling feed for the pigs.

From Winterbrook Farm some twelve hundred acres are now farmed around Blewbury, stretching from the furthest point on the Downs (where three hundred and sixty acres are rented from the racing stables) to the Mill Stream at the lower end of Sheencroft Farm. Ours

Harvest field below Blewburton Hill in 1885/6.

© ASTONS HISTORY GROUP

Harvest field below Blewburton Hill 2005.

© BERNARD MATTIMORE

A Berkshire wagon built in 1875

The Waggon Maker

I have made tales in verse, but this man made
Waggons of elm to last a hundred years;
The blacksmith forged the rims and iron gears,
His was the magic that the wood obeyed.

Each deft device that country wisdom bade,
Or farmers' practice needed, he preserved.
He wrought the subtle contours, straight and curved,
Only by eye, and instinct of the trade.

No weakness, no offence in any part,
It stood the strain in mired fields and roads
In all a century's struggle for its bread;
Bearing, perhaps, eight thousand heavy loads.
Beautiful always as a work of art,
Homing the bride, and harvest, and men dead.

JOHN MASEFIELD (1878-1967)

© BERNARD MATTIMORE

Pre-war binder at work.
Two Shire horses could cut a few acres a day at best, binding the corn into sheaves to be stood in "stooks", like the one on the left, waiting to be carted in for threshing.

is a long, narrow farm with many different soil types and each part of the farm has its own crop rotation. On the Downs we grow wheat, barley, beans and grass. Grass is the main break crop (giving a break from cereals) for this poor, flinty soil and this is grazed and utilised by four hundred ewes which normally lamb in March/April.

The block of ground from the A417 up to the Downs is rolling chalk, fairly free draining, and is cropped with wheat, barley and grass as a break crop. This is utilised by three hundred and fifty sows as an outdoor pig unit. The pigs are born in huts in the fields, reared at Whiteshoot and finished at Winterbrook Farm.

© CLAIRE DE BACKER

A steam traction engine and threshing machine in action.

The land which lies between the A417 and the stream at Sheencroft again varies in soil type. Starting with chalky soils near the A417 and moving on to a heavy loam towards Sheencroft, passing through a vein of greensand in the middle of Sheencroft and on to black, alluvial soil following the Mill Stream. This block of ground is mainly just in arable rotation, growing winter wheat for two years, barley and a break crop of either beans or oilseed rape for one year each.

© BERNARD MATTIMORE

Combine Harvester 2005
This machine can easily harvest eighty acres in one day.

All the grain from these farms is stored at Winterbrook Farm; half of it is fed back to the pigs and the other half sold. The only grazing around Winterbrook Farm is in the paddocks nearest the farm buildings and of course on Blewburton Hill. This is lightly grazed, sometimes by sheep but more often by cattle, which are from our dairy herd at West Hagbourne.

Ever since the Allen family have owned Blewburton Hill it has only been grazed by livestock. As far as we know none of it has ever been ploughed although the grass on top of the hill is a more productive and lush grass than that on the steps and banks where there is a more scrubby, downland type of grass. We try not to overgraze the Hill by not putting too many cattle there at any one time because of the damage caused by their hooves when following each other up and down the hill. From past experience we have always encountered problems with the public and their dogs when we put sheep on the Hill (we have actually lost a number of sheep there) so we try not to graze sheep there too often.

GROWING MORE

During the First and Second World Wars the UK became desperately short of food, which then led to food rationing, rationing books and controls on farm gate prices. The UK had neglected its agriculture in favour of imports of higher quality products from its Commonwealth countries: ie wheat from Canada, lamb from New Zealand and beef from Australia. Due to the war, these food supplies could no longer get through and it was Winston Churchill who said that we should no longer be reliant on other parts of the world for our food. From then on, subsidies were paid to farmers to produce food for the nation. Grants were also offered to farmers to drain fields, grub out hedges and make fields bigger, and to put in up-to-date buildings for grain storage and dairying.

A large amount of money was also invested in research and development in agriculture to enable farmers to grow intensively clean fields of wheat, barley, potatoes and grass, using artificial fertilisers and modern day chemicals. The development of modern farm equipment has also played a large part in mechanising the cultivation of the soil.

Breeding ewes today consistently produce and rear two lambs or more.

There has been a huge genetic improvement in all species of farm livestock, including bigger, more productive dairy cows solely for the production of milk, the introduction of high quality, continental, crossbred beef animals to produce the good quality beef that we now expect, pigs that will produce extra piglets per sow and the production of pig meat with little fat, and breeding ewes to consistently produce and rear two lambs or more.

GROWING TOO MUCH

All this of course has led to UK agriculture becoming one of the most efficient in the world, but in turn has resulted in too much food being produced. We now find ourselves in a situation where modern day agriculture is being less supported in terms of subsidies and becoming inefficient in terms of trading at world market prices because of our very high labour and fixed costs structure. So perhaps we will be considering growing other things in the future: we might be covering the fields with energy giving crops that can be used for fuel, possibly in power stations, such as willow coppicing, or trying oil producing crops that could potentially fuel cars etc.

One thing we have introduced in and around Winterbrook Farm is the use of organic, arable cropping using no fertilisers or sprays. So if, around June time, some of our fields do not look quite as weed free as they have done in the past, it is for that reason. We have been organic farming to some extent for a number of years but, as a result of recent publicity, a number of other people are now growing crops organically and the premium market is not there any more.

Our balanced farming system using livestock as part of the rotation enables us to utilise the farmyard manure and slurry to help produce and grow crops as well, if not better than our competitors and also keeps the soil structure in good heart at the same time.

Over the years one of the biggest changes in agriculture has been in arable farming. In the 1950s my father was farming his acreage with tractors of some 60 horsepower; the work is now being done with 200 horsepower tractors. He would be harvesting with three combine harvesters, cutting approximately ten acres each per day. We now have one combine that will easily harvest 80 acres in one working day. My father would have ploughed 100% of the farm and nearly all of it would have been drilled in the spring. Today we only plough 25% of the farm and 90% of the planting takes place in the autumn. Back in the 50s my father employed ten men to farm 500 acres. We now at Winterbrook employ eight full time men and a student to farm all the enterprises in an area of 1200 acres plus some contract work.

Another huge difference between my father's farming in the 50s and now is the vast amount of paperwork required by DEFRA, Brussels and the individual enterprise schemes: i.e. dairy, beef and lamb and combinable crops, along with the increased pressures from Health and Safety and the requirement for continuous training of staff. Recently introduced Nitrogen Vulnerable Zones (which require strict monitoring of farmyard manures on to the soil), the Waste Management Scheme, monitoring of all buildings containing asbestos etc all create enormous amounts of paperwork.

It is hardly surprising that so many small farmers are disappearing and the bigger farms are getting bigger. Many farms now have to find alternative ways of generating income, whether it be by converting barns into houses, office lets, light industrial use, storage, stabling, bed and breakfast or even by creating golf courses, because of the decline in agricultural incomes. These changes have occurred because we are now in a world market situation and the majority of the food consumed in the UK is once again coming from different parts of the world. They are, of course, being driven by the supermarkets and their quest to supply cheaper and cheaper food. Clearly with our cost structure we cannot compete and as a knock-on effect there are very few young farmers coming into the industry, our agricultural colleges are becoming few and far between, and our general rural infrastructure is in decline.

Expectations of people living in the country have changed dramatically. People with more time on their hands now require more leisure pursuits and the freedom to walk and wander at will. We at Winterbrook Farm appreciate that Blewburton Hill is a popular local facility, and we respect and maintain the footpaths there. Providing that visitors too respect the needs of a working farm and the codes of the countryside, we are happy for the public to enjoy the walk and splendid views from this outstanding place, part of our local heritage.

ANTHONY AND CAROL ALLEN, WINTERBROOK FARM

PHILLIP WRIGHT FIRST PUBLISHED THE TRACTION ENGINE PICTURE IN *TRACTION ENGINES* 1959.

THE ASSISTANCE OF ACTON SCOTT HISTORIC WORKING FARM, SHROPSHIRE, IN ALLOWING AND HELPING WITH PHOTOGRAPHY, IS GRATEFULLY ACKNOWLEDGED.

THE ASTONS HISTORY GROUP KINDLY GAVE PERMISSION TO PUBLISH THE 1885/86 "CURRY" PHOTOGRAPH. THE PHOTOGRAPHER IS BELIEVED TO BE THE REVEREND CURRY OF THE ASTONS.

THE POEM *THE WAGGON MAKER* IS REPRODUCED BY KIND PERMISSION OF THE SOCIETY OF AUTHORS ON BEHALF OF THE ESTATE OF JOHN MASEFIELD.

© Peter Cockrell

Recent Natural History

In the Blewbury region, the scarp slope of the chalk downs provides an important area for chalk grassland. However, much of the scarp here is north facing and therefore relatively cool. Moreover most areas have been agriculturally improved with applications of fertilizer and herbicides, and are no longer species-rich. Calcareous grassland carries an outstandingly high number of species of plants and invertebrates, some of which are very rare. For this reason chalk grassland is recognized as a nationally important habitat for wildlife, and is a Biodiversity Action Plan Priority habitat.

The slopes of Blewburton hillfort and its lynchets constitute a significant area of high quality chalk grassland. The hill is an outlier of the chalk and so has south-facing slopes which provide a more temperate habitat for warmth requiring species and for butterflies. The particularly steep slopes are inaccessible to farm machinery, thus escaping "improvement". The slopes have a great diversity of flowers such as rockrose, common wild thyme, clustered bellflower, bird's-foot trefoil, stemless thistle, field scabious, woolly thistle, cowslip, musk thistle, bulbous buttercup, hop trefoil, hoary plantain, salad burnet, hare-bell and glaucous sedge. The sward is also rich in grasses with sheep's fescue, quaking grass, upright brome grass, common bent and crested dog's tail. The level areas of the lynchets have fewer species with abundant cock's-foot grass and some white and red clover.

In a few areas, nutrient build up has occurred, which encourages the growth of stinging nettles and thistles. Where the ground is disturbed, for instance by rabbits and paths, there are annual plants such as the pink flowered field madder. Many such annuals are declining nationally as arable fields become clean of weeds.

The grazing on this grassland is essential to maintain the rich variety of plants, which would otherwise be out competed by dense grass growth. Cattle grazing is particularly interesting as it leads to more gaps in the sward that can be utilized by annuals.

A few hawthorn bushes are present and these are important especially to songbirds who use them as perches from which to defend

(Top): Agrimony; Clustered Bellflower; Common Restharrow; and Bird's Foot Trefoil, Eggs 'n' Bacon or Tom Thumb.

their territories. Two walnut trees form a distinctive feature. These are not native and have probably been planted, but perhaps brought by rooks or grey squirrels.

A more gently sloping strip of grassland to the east is also very species-rich, with frequent yellow-wort, carline thistle, agrimony, lady's bedstraw, wild parsnip, common restharrow, pepper saxifrage, fairy flax, mouse-ear hawkweed, hop trefoil, greater knapweed and field scabious. The latter two are important nectar sources for a range of butterflies and other insects. Butterflies on the area include large skipper and small heath, while the speckled bush cricket has been recorded as has the unusual heath snail *Helicella itala*. Badger, rabbit and brown hare all make their homes here.

The rare squinancy wort has been recorded in the past. Other species, also recorded some time ago, include pyramidal orchid, common broomrape, dropwort, dwarf spurge, small scabious, field rose, sweet vernal grass, downy oat-grass, meadow oat-grass, yellow oat-grass, crested hair grass, kidney vetch and horseshoe vetch. The latter two are important food plants for small blue and chalkhill blue butterflies; these rare species are not currently known at the site but do occur in the area, and might recolonise if conditions were suitable.

CAMILLA LAMBRICK
BERKSHIRE, BUCKINGHAMSHIRE AND OXFORDSHIRE WILDLIFE TRUST

© PETER COCKRELL

(Top): Field Scabious or Gypsy Rose; Dropwort; Common Rock Rose; and Cowslip.

A Nature Walk

The Iron Age hill fort at Blewburton lies along a wildlife corridor that crosses downland and lowland and so is in a good position to support and welcome both plant and animal life. Walk up there on a summer's morning as the sun rises. Close your eyes and you can almost see and hear those ancient settlers coming along the track. Open your eyes and the scene before you would, in part, have been recognisable to them: cattle grazing down below, the odd hare nibbling at the herbs, maybe a buzzard swooping down, snails, insects, worms. There is a rich world at your feet. The plant life of the chalk grassland on the steep slopes of the fort would have been known to those people, though not by today's names; they dwelt here long before botanical records were kept. They would probably have sorted out which plants were useful and which were poisonous to man. Plants with which they may have been familiar are those which survived the last Ice Age and once grew in semi-arctic grassland. These plants were not smothered when Britain later became covered in forests.

SOME ANCIENT PLANTS

Such a plant is Salad Burnet or Poor Man's Pepper, *Sanguisorba minor*; its cucumber flavoured leaves might have enlivened a monotonous diet. It does not tolerate grazing but is safe from cattle on the steeper slopes.

The Picnic or Stemless Thistle, *Cirsium acaule*, is noted for its appearance on Iron Age ramparts. It tolerates grazing, hardly surprising since it lies flat on the ground. Tread carefully as only its purple flower will reveal this hidden, prickly customer.

Fairy Flax or Purging Flax, *Linum catharticum*, is another survivor. You could be forgiven for not spotting this tiny plant. It was probably known to Iron Age Man but, unlike the later people of the seventeenth century, it is doubtful if they cooked it in white wine to make an effective purgative.

Bird's-foot Trefoil, *Lotus corniculatus*, has been around for a very long time. Not only do counts of pollen grains preserved in ancient soils reveal its age, but also the fact that it has over seventy different

© PETER COCKRELL

(Top): Greater Knapweed; parasitic Broomrape, with its host Greater Knapweed; Lady's Bedstraw with Pyramidal Orchid; and Hoary Plantain.

local names. In Oxfordshire it was known as Tom Thumb. Why is it called bird's-foot? Look at its claw-like fruit pods.

Another survivor is the Common Rock Rose, *Helianthemum nummulariam*, with its pretty yellow flowers. It is the ancestor of our chalk-loving garden rock roses. Wild Parsnip, *Pastinaca sativa*, not surprisingly persisted in arctic conditions at low altitude. It has a tough, stringy root that would not be pleasant to eat. Self Heal, *Prunella vulgaris*, as its name suggests, was used as a medicine. It emerged from the last Ice Age and escaped the shade of later dense woodland.

Much of our woodland, the Wildwood of long ago, was cut down to make way for farming, by Neolithic man, so that by the Iron Age much of the tree cover had gone. Many plants arrived here with those tillers of the land, accompanying their rather low-yielding cereals Plantains most likely were brought over by them and have invaded farmland, paths and tracks ever since. They are not killed by trampling, grazing or mowing. The most attractive of the plantains is Hoary Plantain, *Plantago media*, with its pink, silvery flower heads. Pollen from Ribgrass, *Plantago lanceolata*, causes hay fever but this does not stop children playing with it. Traditionally children used to name the flower heads Black Man, Soldier, Hardhead and Fighting Cock; they had fights with them, to see which one kept its head longest.

Some plants that we call weeds could have come here with the crops of early farmers or on their feet or those of their animals. Many of these are annuals that seed out each year then die; they find homes where the ground has been dug by rabbits, birds or man. They cannot compete with dense grasses. In loose earth, plants such as Shepherd's Purse, *Capsella bursa-pastoris*, another Ice Age survivor, and Common Chickweed, *Stellaria media*, which tolerates intense cold, sow their seeds successfully. The Pink Flowered Field Madder, Sheradia arvensis, can be found appearing each spring. It is not a plant easily spotted so all credit is due to William Sherard, a botanist who was born in 1659, after whom it was named. He must have been very observant.

PLANTS TO REDISCOVER

Our hill fort today needs some observant plant spotters to explore carefully the steep, grassy slopes. The flat terraces are not particularly

© PETER COCKRELL

(Top): Self Heal; Salad Burnet or Poor Man's Pepper; Red Clover, the bee's favourite but in short supply today; and Sainfoin.

(Top): the rare Squinancywort flowering with Common Wild Thyme; White Clover; and Stemless or Picnic Thistle.

© Peter Cockrell

rewarding to plant spotters as they support abundant cocksfoot grass and some red and white clover. Several plants that grew on the banks fifteen years ago have not been spotted recently, but there is no reason why they should not return. Keep your eyes open for Horseshoe Vetch, *Hippocrepis comosa*, a plant indicator of ancient grassland, last seen here in 1986. It can be recognised by its distinctive fruit pods - a chain of little "horseshoes". Kidney Vetch, *Anthyllis vulnararia*, has not been recorded since 1991. Both these vetches are the food plants for the blue and chalkhill blue butterflies. If the vetches reappeared up there so would the butterflies.

Search too for Common Broomrape, *Orobanche minor*, last recorded in 1986. It is a parasite living off other plants and is not too fussy, but generally prefers legumes, members of the pea family. Squinancywort, *Asperula cynanchica*, again was last recorded in 1986. What a fascinating name this is and a curious plant; it would be rewarding if it turned up again. In 1570 it was found growing on the man-made, steep, chalky slopes of Silbury Hill! It was valued as a gargle for quinsy (tonsillitis) and sore throats.

One observant Blewbury plant spotter was Job Lousley 1790-1855; he noted the locations of plants he observed in and around Blewbury. He was the great-great grandfather of the famous botanist Job Edward Lousley (Uncle Ted). Ted was inspired as a little boy when he came across his ancestor's notes and he himself became the author of that beloved and unique book the New Naturalist "Wild Flowers of the Chalk and Limestone".

A WILDLIFE COMMUNITY

Dotted about the hill are Hawthorn bushes which could be the descendants of those trees which marked the Anglo Saxon parish boundaries of Blewbury, recorded in 944 AD "...Along the stoneway to the crucifix at the Hawk-thorn; then from Hawk-thorn to the long thorn at Icknield way; so to the third thorn at Wirhangra ..." Blewburton hill lies within this extensive boundary. Hawthorn, with its May blossom, heralds the spring and for this reason is associated with magic. In autumn, the red haws or fruits are food for birds which spread the seeds. Hawthorn can quickly cover the slopes in scrub; a balanced population of rabbits will control this spread. However too many rabbits will eat and destroy the variety of precious herb plants. Foxes will keep the rabbit population in balance. Look out for the odd black rabbit and also the recently introduced black pheasant.

Within this community, all the plants and animals depend on each other. Some of the flowering plants depend on bees, flies and butterflies to bring pollen from flowers nearby. Of these, the butterflies are the most spectacular and colourful but the men of the Iron Age had little time to appreciate them. They would have been aware of them though, because some species of butterfly arrived in Britain in late glacial times. Of those that we call British butterflies the Large White, *Pieris brassicae*, Small White, *Pieris rapae*, and the Green-veined White, *Pieris napi*, that have been resident here for ages, still are invaded from time to time by migrants from across the continent. The Brimstone butterfly, *Gonepteryx rhamni*, is a butterfly of antiquity; the bright yellow-winged male can be spotted on a spring day. Later in the summer the Red Admiral, *Vanessa atalanta*, can be seen but this is a migrant that does not take kindly to our climate though like the Small Tortoiseshell, *Aglais urticae*, they try to hibernate with some success.

Some recent invaders are less welcome; Oxford ragwort, *Senecio squalidus*, escaped from the Oxford Botanic gardens in the late eighteenth century and has spread rapidly recently. It is toxic to grazing animals if dried with grass for hay. Another unwelcome invader is the Muntjac deer, which though not often seen on the hill, can travel across its terrain seeking vulnerable garden and farm crops. An unexpected plant is the Walnut *Juglans*, probably carried there by rooks, crows or squirrels from down below in the village, where trees remain from the once profitable crops grown there.

BERNARDINE SHIRLEY-SMITH, AUTHOR OF *THE SECRET LIFE OF A GARDEN* AND OTHER WORKS.

© PETER COCKRELL

(Top): Common Wild Thyme; Yellow Wort; and Hare Bell.

ORCHIDS OF THE DOWNS

© PETER COCKRELL

© CHRIS RAPER

© NICK CARTHEY

(Top): Pyramidal Orchid, colour varying from deep pink to (rarely) white; Common Spotted Orchid; and Fragrant Orchid.

Many people think of orchids as the exotic tropical blooms you may see in garden centres, but in fact Britain can boast over fifty species of orchids. Quite a few of these occur on the downlands of Oxfordshire and Berkshire, as chalk soil provides a suitable habitat for many of our British orchids. I have chosen to describe five of the more easily observed species, which occur in our area with one less common and two extremely rare species, which have to be protected to ensure their survival.

PYRAMIDAL ORCHID

The Pyramidal Orchid is perhaps the typical orchid of dry chalk downlands, with it's distinctive pyramidal flower spike, the colour varying from deep pink to (rarely) white. In Oxfordshire it is also a relatively common sight on road verges and roundabouts during June and July. It can be quite abundant when growing in its favoured habitats.

COMMON SPOTTED ORCHID

The Common Spotted Orchid keeps company with the Pyramidal Orchid and the Bee Orchid, but it can also tolerate much damper and shadier habitats such as woodlands. The over all colour of the flower spike is most commonly pink, but the lip of the flower in typical plants has a distinctive dark pink double loop. Relatively variable in appearance however, on occasion deep red and white forms with no distinct markings are found. The leaves usually have characteristic brownish blotches or spots, although sometimes specimens with unspotted leaves may be found. The flowering period is quite long, from mid-May to July.

FRAGRANT ORCHID

Rather more local in our area, is the Fragrant Orchid. However, I know a site where it grows on chalk grassland in the presence of a grazing herd of cows, with Pyramidal Orchids also occurring nearby. This orchid has a distinctive pink flower spike (sometimes white) and the three-lobed shape of the individual flower is also characteristic. This orchid is now considered to occur as three distinct species, each having slightly different sweet scents, as suggested by the common name. Pollination is by butterflies and day-flying moths. In our area, this orchid is in flower during June.

Bee Orchid

The Bee Orchid is perhaps our most well loved orchid, the flower resembling some kind of furry bumblebee. It is a member of the "insect-mimicking" orchids, of which there are four species in Britain. The flowers of these orchids have evolved to tempt male insects to "mate" with what it thinks is a female bee, and thus transfer pollen to other plants. However, in this country, it is known that the bee orchid is almost always self-pollinated. The bee orchid is not very obvious from a distance, so you need to "get your eye in", and then you may spot several in the same area. It is by no means as common as the Pyramidal or Common Spotted Orchids, but frequently grows in the vicinity of these other species. June and July are the usual flowering time for the bee orchid.

White Helleborine

The White Helleborine is a member of the orchid group known as helleborines in which there are about twelve species in Britain. It will not usually be found on open downland, but rather under the dark beech woodland with little ground cover which borders the downs in certain areas. It is perhaps not quite so "orchid-like" as the species described above, having ivory-white flowers carried upright on the stem. The flowers do not open widely, but a yellow "lip" can be seen within. Flowering period: May to June.

Twayblade

This is a fairly common orchid although it is hard to find with its generally green and well-camouflaged appearance. It has a liking for damp woods and meadows. When examined closely it has extremely dainty, fairylike flowers.

(Top): Bee Orchid; White Helleborine; and Twayblade.

© PETER COCKRELL

© PETER COCKRELL

(Above): Lady Orchid; (right):
Monkey Orchid.

MONKEY ORCHID

The Monkey Orchid is extremely rare and we are very fortunate to have obtained a picture. It is not easily spotted among the rich flora of sunny, chalk grassland. The charming flower is unusual in that it opens from the top downwards. It appears in May when the little "monkeys" can be seen dancing in the breeze.

LADY ORCHID

Only slightly less rare in our area is the Lady Orchid. Flowering in May, in chalk woodland or scrub, it sports tiny "ladies" in spotted, pink dresses with dark red hoods.

NICK CARTHEY

A Bird's Eye View

The Past

Forty years ago, a solitary
Buzzard circling high above
Blewburton Hill sees happy
hunting grounds all around. To
the southwest lies the vast open
expanse of Churn. Then, turning
anti-clockwise, come Aston
Upthorpe Downs and Juniper
Valley with Lowbury Hill beyond.
Further east are the Fairmile and

The Red Kite.

Kingstanding Hill with the Well Barn Estate extending to the south.
Next comes Lollingdon Hill, an outcrop of the Berkshire Downs similar
to Blewburton Hill, while north of Lollingdon lie Cholsey Hill and the
Wittenham Clumps.

All of these downland areas have a history of playing host to some
special birds, species that are not only scarce nationally, but that might
also arouse the interest of the non birdwatcher. Quail, Stone Curlew,
Long-eared Owl, Red-backed Shrike, Cirl Bunting, and Nightjar were
regularly to be found breeding somewhere in our Buzzard's world.
Up until 1953 the Corncrake could have been added to this impressive
list. Over-wintering Hen Harriers; Short-eared Owls, and Merlins
maintained all year interest.

On rare occasions in winter you could have found the Mountain
Linnet or Twite at Churn or a huge flock of Lapwing above Compton
(2,000 in 1965) or Aston Tirrold and Cholsey Downs (tens of thousands
in 1966). Generally, records tended to come from the better-watched
areas such as Churn, Fairmile and Aston Upthorpe Downs. If, as it
seems, bird recorders seldom visited Blewburton Hill, it is hard to
imagine that this promontory would not have entertained some of
these birds at times.

In more recent years there have been other exciting records. Ring
Ouzels on passage above Aston Upthorpe and a Great Grey Shrike

on Lollingdon Hill. There was even a successful breeding of the rare Montagu's Harrier in 1986.

THE PRESENT

Today birds of prey abound over Blewburton Hill. Outside the breeding season, several Buzzards and Red Kites float in the thermals, and playfully spar with Kestrels, Rooks and Jackdaws. The latter two species are arguably the most widespread in the area, and so have been chosen here to represent our everyday birds. One reason for the dramatic increase in raptors is that Buzzards have spread from the South West at a remarkable rate. Forty years ago there were less than thirty records a year for Oxfordshire and Berkshire combined. By the year 2000, the number of records for Oxfordshire alone had risen to over 740.

Just a few years ago the RSPB, with key assistance from landowner Sir Paul Getty, reintroduced the Red Kite to the Chilterns. The success of this initiative is plain for all to see. So now it is the Red Kite that is most likely to be seen floating idly over Blewburton Hill. Long wings and a forked tail help identification even at a distance. Just possibly the Kite might catch sight of Short-eared Owls (that wintered around the Wittenham Clumps in 2004/5); a Hen Harrier (still occasionally seen in the Churn/Chilton area); or Stone Curlews (the RSPB are having some success in encouraging suitable habitats for this strange bird).

The odd Quail can still be heard, and the Merlin remains a rare winter visitor. As for other special birds that once graced the local Downs, they may be gone for ever. One question springs to mind here - why was this area so rich in bird life not protected in some way? Surely it should have been.

But all is not gloom and doom. Looking towards the hills, our Kite can see that Corn Buntings survive in good numbers. This local speciality, with its distinctive reeling call a little like an old fashioned football rattle, can be seen perched on any post or other vantage point. The Downs also support good numbers of small passerines such as

Montagu's Harrier, painted by Ian Lewington.

Merlin, painted by Ian Lewington.

Corn Bunting, painted by Ian Lewington

Linnet, Meadow Pipit, and Whitethroat. Ever since a pair of Peregrines chose Didcot Power Station as their base, there is the chance of seeing one of these dashing falcons. Stonechats seem to have discovered Churn. Fieldfares abound in winter, when modest Lapwing flocks may still be seen also at Churn. Wheatears stop on passage, Blewburton's strip lynchets offering them an ideal resting place. A search of fields and hedges surrounding Blewburton Hill is likely to yield Skylarks, Grey Partridges, Lesser Black-backed Gulls, Yellowhammers, and for the observant only - a resting Little Owl.

Focusing on White Hollow Way, leading above Aston Upthorpe to the Downs, the Kite may find breeding Lesser Whitethroat, Willow Warbler, Chiffchaff, Blackcap and even Turtle Dove. This is a real birding hotspot, well worth a stroll up from the Astons.

(Above): Skylark; (left): Yellowhammer.

VILLAGE BIRDS

Our reintroduced raptor has more of an eye for the local communities than the Buzzard ever had, so naturally his gaze will fall on Blewbury and the Astons. Both are blessed with plenty of old buildings, native

(Above): Goldfinch; (right): Song Thrush.

©Tony Rayner

trees and hedges, large gardens, old orchards, and streams, well populated by favourites such as the robins and blue tits. It is not surprising, therefore, to find also some more noteworthy birds in residence here.

In Blewbury, one observer has kept detailed bird records since 1987. She includes Kingfishers and both Green and Great Spotted Woodpeckers as regulars. The Tawny Owl and Grey Wagtail are among her "occasionals". She has not heard a Cuckoo in Blewbury since 1999; sadly, she is not alone. A worse tale of woe surrounds the Swift. In summer the air around the Barley Mow was filled with screaming parties of Swifts. They used to nest under the eaves of Tudor Cottage. The owner of this lovely old cottage noticed that they failed to return about five years ago and have not been seen since. The same thing happened at Ickleton House, a little further along the same road. No changes were made to the cottages that could have driven these wonderful fliers from what may be their last breeding site in either Blewbury or the Astons.

From Bessels Way in Blewbury, one bird watcher regards House Sparrows as regular visitors. Elsewhere searches for these once abundant birds only bore fruit at Forge House in Westbrook Street and Pound Furlong beside London Road. Our bird watcher provides both nesting boxes and bird food, something perhaps for others to consider. My Blewbury birding hotspot is the churchyard. The abundance of cover is such that, in order to see anything at all, one should approach slowly or rest awhile until the birds come out of hiding. This is a great place to find the elusive Song Thrush.

Turning to the Astons, feeding stations seem to attract all the House Sparrows (Dashwood and no. 1 Baker St.) and Goldfinches (Upper Thorpe). Not only have the owners of the latter seemingly hijacked all the Goldfinches, but also they report a regular autumn sighting in their garden of a Wood Warbler, which obviously has good taste. Tree Creepers, Woodpeckers, Redwing and Kingfishers are recorded from The Smithy in Thorpe Street. The Kingfishers are almost certainly attracted by the stream that flows from a spring in this two-acre garden. For me, the Astons' number one bird was the House Martin; the sky was just full of them. Thank goodness people, such as the owner of Little Gables, tolerate their nests - much to the annoyance of a local black and white cat! For myself I can add Sparrowhawk to the Aston Upthorpe list - one flashed by the path from Picks to Thorpe Street. In Aston Tirrold, Coal Tits and Goldcrests lurked in the St Michael's Churchyard conifers.

Birds seen in the villages, but appearing to show no particular bias for either Blewbury or the Astons, included Bullfinches, Swallows and Long-tailed Tits. Similarly, I too hope to have shown no undue bias in writing this article, and hope to have given a flavour of the avian treasures to be found in the area - past and present.

TONY RAYNER

HISTORICAL SOURCE - OXFORD ORNITHOLOGICAL SOCIETY ANNUAL BIRD REPORTSACKNOWLEDGEMENTS. THE GENEROSITY OF IAN LEWINGTON IN ALLOWING THE REPRODUCTION OF HIS PAINTINGS IS GRATEFULLY ACKNOWLEDGED.
ALSO BRIAN BARNACLE, THE RSPB AND GIGRIN FARM VERY KINDLY PROVIDED THE EXCELLENT PHOTOGRAPHS OF BIRDS.
THANKS ARE ALSO DUE TO: JOANNA THOMSON, MR F. SHARRAT. BRENDA HOPKINS, SHIRLEY KAY, TOM AND JENNY WORTHINGTON AND MARIE MARKS FOR THEIR OBSERVATIONS AND NOTES.

GRASSLAND BUTTERFLIES OF THE AREA

Butterflies form part of a large family of insects, the Lepidoptera, which includes both moths and butterflies. There are some 2,500 species of Lepidoptera in Britain, sixty of these are butterflies and forty-five are regularly seen in the Thames Valley counties of Berkshire, Buckinghamshire and Oxfordshire. Of these, thirty-eight species are regularly recorded within five miles of Blewburton Hill including thirty-five resident species. Butterflies are generally easy to identify being day flying, relatively large and often brightly or distinctively coloured. Being a popular group there are several good identification guides available.

Only the thirty-three local species (thirty residents) normally seen

(Clockwise from top left): Comma; Large White; Small Tortoiseshell; Small White; Peacock,; Red Admiral; Green-Veined White.

flying in grassland habitats are covered in this article. These include twenty generalists and ten species that have more specialist habitat requirements, some of these being rare. The rare species are usually only found in higher quality nature conservation habitats. The other three species are wholly or partially migratory, and if they breed, they also rely on influxes from Europe to sustain or enhance their populations.

WHITES, YELLOWS, BROWNS, SKIPPERS AND BLUES

Some butterflies are more or less ubiquitous, being seen (but not necessarily breeding) in most habitats including grasslands. These include the familiar and colourful Peacock, Small Tortoiseshell, Comma and Red Admiral - and in some years the migratory Painted Lady. Other ubiquitous butterflies include the "Cabbage Whites" a catch-all term for the Large, Small and Green Veined Whites. The other common White is the Orange Tip, which flies in the spring. Only the males have the distinctive orange tip to their wings. The larval food plants of these whites are various species of Crucifer (Cabbage family). Usually the first butterfly to be seen in the spring is the male yellow Brimstone (perhaps the original "butter coloured fly"), with the pale green female appearing a few days later. This is not a grassland species as it lays its eggs on Buckthorns, but is often seen patrolling open habitats.

Long grass is a good habitat for many of the Brown butterflies. Even now, some of these are still abundant in the countryside; anywhere that is, where grass is not heavily managed. The most common of the species are the Meadow Brown and Hedge Brown (or Gatekeeper). More typically found in better downland habitats is the

(Clockwise from top left): Painted Lady; Marbled White (female above); Brimstone; Meadow Brown; Small Skipper; Orange Tip; and Hedge Brown.

*(Top): Dingy Skipper; Silver
Spotted Skipper; Large Skipper;
Grizzled Skipper; Brown Argus;
Small Blue; and Common Blue.*

black and white Marbled White, which has spread in recent years to many other, less good, grassland areas.

The moth-like Skipper butterflies are all typical of grassland habitats. The three orange species, the Small, Large and Essex Skippers, are common and most at home in rough, often tussocky grassland. In chalk grassland sites they are often found in the more lightly grazed or otherwise un-intensively managed grasslands, perhaps at the bottom of slopes where grass grows thicker because of the greater depth of soil. The Small and Large Skipper are long established native species with the Essex, being a more recent colonist. It has become widespread in the last twenty years having colonised from eastern England. However, it may have been overlooked for several years because of its close similarity to the Small Skipper. Perhaps the easiest way to tell the two apart is the amount of black on the tip of the antennae and the position and angle of the dark scent mark (on males only).

The other three species of Skipper in our area are mostly found in unimproved chalk grassland habitats. The Dingy Skipper is nowhere as dull as its name suggests, bearing a rich red brown pattern. It inhabits shorter grassland, with males using areas of bare ground for displaying. The larvae feed on Bird's Foot Trefoil, a common and widespread plant found on many grasslands. The other, non-orange Skipper, the Grizzled, is a small, smart, black and white butterfly whose larvae feed on Wild Strawberry, a plant found in bare areas such as rabbit scrapes and in wood edges and woodland glades. Perhaps in the past, before we created a landscape dominated by large expanses of grassland, this species was equally at home in open woodland habitats. The last Skipper, the Silver Spotted, is rare and found in only a few south-facing areas of chalk grassland. Traditionally it preferred shorter grassland, with large areas of bare ground and very sparse short tufts of grass, but is now spreading into longer grassland.

Grassland habitats are home to several species of Blue butterflies. Probably the most prevalent is the Common Blue, another species whose larvae feed on Bird's Foot Trefoil. The males of this species have bright blue upper wings, whereas the females are mostly brown, or a mixture of blue and brown. Despite its name the Brown Argus is also in the Blue family - with both sexes being predominantly brown with no blue at all. It is possible to confuse it with small, bright, all brown, female Common Blues. Brown Argus larvae feed on a variety of plants including Common Rockrose, a feature of shorter unimproved limestone chalk grassland habitats. However, it is not confined to these habitats as its larvae also feed on a variety of plants including Cranesbills (Geranium species), thus allowing it to live in other open habitats such as waste ground.

The other species of Blues are either uncommon or rare, and occur in better quality grassland habitats. The Small Blue is the smallest British butterfly; found only where its larval foodplant, Kidney Vetch, grows. This plant is more at home on coastal and cliff grasslands and struggles to survive in many inland grasslands. The Chalkhill Blue can be locally plentiful, but is confined to south facing slopes of unimproved chalk grassland where its larval food plant (Horseshoe Vetch) grows. The Adonis Blue is rarer still, sharing the same larval food plant, but only found in our area in grassland sites in the Goring Gap. Short turf is essential for both these species because they require warm ground temperatures - as does the species of ants with which they are associated and rely. The ants protect and nurse their caterpillars and pupae.

OTHER SPECIES

Two widespread species found in short grassland or other open habitats are the stunning orange and black Small Copper whose larvae feed on Docks - and the Small Heath which is most common in very open short swards. The latter is somewhat like a diminutive Meadow Brown and has declined recently for no clear reason. The Wall is another uncommon species, which has declined to such an extent that it is now more likely to be seen in its favoured coastal grasslands, rather than the inland grasslands such as the Downs around Blewbury.

The remaining grassland species are more specialised, with more specific habitat or larval food plant requirements. The Dark Green Fritillary is the only reasonably common member of this group of handsome orange and black butterflies. Its larvae feed on Violets in grassy places, with larger plants preferred. Thus it can be found right up to and in the margins of scrub and woodland. Also happy in these marginal grassland habitats, as well

(Top): Wall Brown; Small Copper; Small Heath; Chalkhill Blue; and Adonis Blue.

as open grasslands, is the Ringlet (a relative of the Meadow Brown). As its name suggests it is patterned with numerous ring markings, on both its upper and lower wings. The Green Hairstreak is a small but unmistakeable species, which has brown on its upper and green on its lower wing surfaces, providing it with superb camouflage when at rest with its wings shut. It is equally at home in open grassland and bushy places. The Duke of Burgundy is another small but handsome species found in rougher grassland and bushy places, where its larvae have a plentiful supply of well-grown Primula plants. Both the last two species (especially the latter) are uncommon and good finds if seen.

The last species is another Yellow butterfly, the migratory Clouded Yellow, a true grassland species. The number of arrivals varies and in some years it is not uncommon. It does breed, the larvae feeding on Clover – but is unable to survive our winters.

Butterflies are relatively well known and studied when compared with other invertebrates in the UK. There are recently published local and national atlases, charting changes in their populations and distributions. However more records and recorders are always welcome, so if you feel the urge to look at your local patch please get involved. There may be as yet undiscovered local hotspots, home perhaps to one or more of the of the rare or declining species. "Butterfly Conservation", the national charity for butterflies and moths, would be glad to receive the records.

(Top left): Dark Green Fritillary; (top right): Clouded Yellow; Ringlets; Duke of Burgundy; and Green Hairstreak.

ROD D'AYALA
POND CONSERVATION, c/o SCHOOL OF BIOLOGICAL AND MOLECULAR SCIENCES,
OXFORD BROOKES UNIVERSITY

ACKNOWLEDGEMENTS
THE BEAUTIFUL PHOTOGRAPHS PROVIDED BY JIM ASHER, AUTHOR OF *THE BUTTERFLIES OF BERKSHIRE, BUCKINGHAMSHIRE AND OXFORDSHIRE* AND OTHER WORKS, ARE GRATEFULLY ACKNOWLEDGED.
THE EXCELLENT *POCKET GUIDE TO THE BUTTERFLIES OF GREAT BRITAIN AND IRELAND*, BY RICHARD LEWINGTON, HAS BEEN USED EXTENSIVELY TO HELP WITH THE CORRECT PRESENTATION OF THESE PICTURES ALTHOUGH "LIFE SIZE" HAS NOT ALWAYS BEEN ACHIEVED.

Before the Roman came to Rye or out to Severn strode,
The rolling English drunkard made the rolling English road.
A reeling road, a rolling road, that rambles round the shire,
And after him the parson ran, the sexton and the squire;
A merry road, a mazy road, and such as we did tread
The night we went to Birmingham by way of Beachy Head.

From "The Rolling English Road" by G.K.Chesterton (1874-1936)

Upper Chance Lane, high on the Berkshire Downs on a frosty morning.

ANCIENT ROADS AND TRACKWAYS

Two of the oldest routes in Britain pass within a couple of miles or so of Blewburton Hill. They are the Ridgeway, which runs along the crest of the northern escarpment of the Berkshire Downs, and the Icknield way running along the foot of the Downs, below the escarpment, just short of Blewburton Hill. These routes are thought to have brought trade and travellers from East Anglia and the coasts of the Wash, south westwards across the country for some two hundred and fifty miles to the south coast of Devon. Today much of their line has been lost but an exceptionally clear stretch is still preserved for about forty miles through the heart of our area.

THE RIDGEWAY

The Ridgeway is the more evocative lane of the two, since above Blewbury and Aston it still keeps its ancient character of a grassy track.

An Ancient Hollow Way in Spring time, a painting by Joan Durbin.

There are, of course, no records of its origin but numerous sites from the Neolithic, Bronze Age, Iron Age and Roman periods lie along its route, a witness to its antiquity. Most dramatic are the series of hillforts set along the line of the escarpment and through some of which the Ridgeway actually once ran. This was always a track for pack animals and pedestrians, but the trade

45

was far reaching. Flint from Grimes Graves in Norfolk, and salt, both moved along it. From Saxon times, a hoard of three hundred and fifty sceatta coins, discovered on the parallel Icknield way at Aston Rowant, came largely from the Rhine mouth area. It was also used, certainly in later centuries, as a drove road, moving vast flocks of sheep whose intertwining tracks are still visible as crop marks in a dry summer.

The surviving part of the Ridgeway today runs from Ivinghoe Beacon in Buckinghamshire to close to Avebury in Wiltshire. Our section of it crosses the Thames at the Goring Gap then heads directly for the Downs and follows the uplands westwards to the White Horse and beyond. It is a popular ramblers' trail, described thus by Kenneth Grahame (author of *Wind in the Willows*) who lived for a decade at Bohams in Blewbury and walked the Ridgeway each day: "Out on that almost trackless expanse of billowy Downs such a track is in some sort humanly companiable; it really seems to lead you by the hand."

THE ICKNIELD WAY

The Icknield Way is the companion route to the Ridgeway, its origins and much of its alignment equally lost in the mists of time. It is thought, however, to have followed roughly the same route as the Ridgeway, sometimes branching away, at others moving closer. Today it crosses the Thames at the Goring Gap, along with the Ridgeway, but at times in the past it took the Moulsford crossing and then Halfpenny Lane. In our area it had two names, the Icknield Way (Icen hilde, the highway of the Celtic Iceni tribe) and Ickleton Way (perhaps from a village near its route). It also had two courses between Upton and Wantage; from the former it branched slightly south along the road towards Chilton, then straightened to run south of Harwell and on through

The Ancient Ridgeway

"Out on that almost trackless expanse of billowy Downs such a track is in some sort humanly companiable; it really seems to lead you by the hand."

Kenneth Grahame (1859-1932)

ANN SETH © COUNTRYSIDE AGENCY

Cow Lane leading to the Downs from Blewbury.

© PETER COCKRELL

Lockinge and Ardington; the other route continued north westwards from Upton via Harwell to Wantage and became known as the Portway, today's A417.

The springline along the northern foot of the Downs escarpment clearly determined the line of the Icknield Way. While the upland Ridgeway was clearer of forest and marsh in ancient times and therefore an easier route, it also lacked water. In summer, the lowland marshes dried out, the springs continued to flow, and a string of villages welcomed the Icknield Way. It was an easier summer route.

The Saxons referred to it as a straet, or street, implying that some of it at least had been metalled in Roman times. It was also known as a herepaeth or "army path". Remains of Saxon warriors buried beside the road may indicate that armies used it to move to and from Saxon strongholds such as Wantage. For the early Normans, the Icknield Way was a major road, one of only four in the land subject to a special order of peaceful usage. In 1804 it was upgraded to a Turnpike Road, the Portway section being chosen rather than the more southerly Icknield section which had been closed across Lockinge Park. The Turnpike, in its turn, formed the basis for much of today's A417, which runs across the ridge of Blewburton Hill, between the hillfort and the Downs.

DROVE ROADS

Drovers taking cattle and sheep to market used the Icknield Way for many centuries. Halfpenny Lane is an old drove road, leading south from the Fair Mile, that branches off the A 417 at the five-point crossroads at the top of Kingstanding Hill. It was part of a drove road that ran from Wales and the West Country towards London and was also used to take sheep up across the Downs to the large annual sheep fair at East Ilsley where eighty thousand sheep were traded in a season. Drovers used Halfpenny Lane to reach the ford across the Thames at Moulsford, to the north of Streatley.

So rovers followed both the Ridgeway across the Downs and the old Icknield Way past Blewburton Hill. The name Halfpenny Lane may be associated with a halfpenny "drove" pound, which was where a drover could rest his sheep in an enclosure, for the price of half a penny per beast per night. Local

(Overleaf):
John Rocque Map, 1761
In 1750 only small parts of England had been mapped in any detail. John Rocque, "Topographer to His Majesty George III", was one of the first county surveyors. By 1761 he had mapped Shropshire, Middlesex and Berkshire as well as Dublin and Armagh in Ireland at the one-inch scale. The surveying was probably done by road-traverse using compass and wheel-perambulator. This was as good as early triangulation methods and much cheaper. It was not until around the 1820s that the military based Ordnance Survey competed successfully with private county surveyors like Rocque.

From John Rocque's map of Berkshire 1761, one of the first detailed county maps in England.

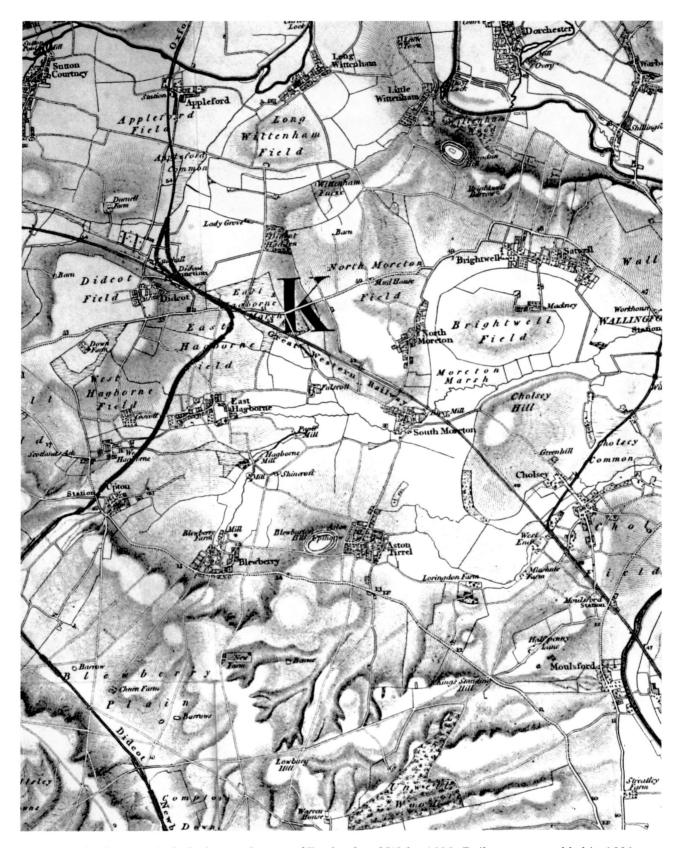

From the first one-inch Ordnance Survey of England and Wales 1830. Railways were added in 1891.

Turnpike Charges at Streatley 1804
Charges for the use of this turnpike in 1804 were set at:
- *Coach with four wheels six pence*
- *Coach with less than four wheels - three pence*
- *Wagon or cart with four wheels - four pence*
- *Wagon with less than four wheels - two pence*
- *Mare, stallion, gelding or mule unladen - two pence*
- *Cow or meat cattle - a halfpenny*
- *Calf, hog, sheep or lamb - one farthing*

(Previous page):
Ordnance Survey 1830
From the first one-inch Ordnance Survey of England and Wales was published at the Tower of London by Lieutenant Colonel Colby of the Royal Engineers 1st May 1830. The railways were added in 1891.

Measurements were made with compass and wheel within a large triangulated framework. The triangulation work started in 1799.

oral history places a Drovers overnight pound west of Lollingdon Farm (Lulla's settlement – Lulla being a Roman name). The 1794 Aston Upthorpe enclosure map shows a drove road, with another drove pound, running west to east across the north end of the village. This map also marks the Icknield Way as separate from that Drove Road, running where the Turnpike Road (now the A 417) was later built. Drovers tried hard to avoid tolls and may have started using different routes after tolls were introduced.

EIGHTEENTH-CENTURY ROADS AND THE TURNPIKE ACTS

The salient feature of roads through the 16th and 17th century was mud, in great quantities. The 1555 Highways Act made each Parish responsible for the maintenance of roads within its area. Landowners were not prepared to fund repairs to roads used by travellers passing through their land since it brought no advantage to them.

Roads were transformed by the Turnpike Acts. These were acts of parliament allowing groups to set up a Turnpike Trust. In return the Trust upgraded a road and was allowed to erect a number of turnpikes or gates where tolls were charged. The name "turnpike" denotes the earliest form of road barricade – usually a long pike resting on two supports, which could be "turned" or opened. These tolls were extremely unpopular with travellers and drovers.

An ambitious programme of turnpikes was considered by the Besselsleigh Turnpike Trust, set up in 1771 by a group of business men in Wantage. Their plan was to create a north/south and east/west network of roadways with Wantage at the centre. The north/south turnpike ran from Oxford (passing through Besselsleigh to the west of Oxford) via Frilford to Wantage and then on to Hungerford where it ended. An unsuccessful plan proposed a turnpike from Wallingford via Cholsey, crossing Halfpenny Lane, along The Fair Mile, then following the Ridgeway to Wantage to meet the existing north/south turnpike from Oxford to Hungerford.

A Wantage to Wallingford Trust finally turnpiked the Harwell to Streatley road, with construction work commencing in 1804. It is interesting to note that Saxon graves and weapons were found on either side of the road near Blewbury. It improved the old springline route from Harwell to Blewbury. After Blewbury it followed the old Icknield Way crossing Halfpenny Lane at Kingstanding Hill, to meet the Wallingford to Reading Road at Lands End north of Streatley. This followed a similar plan originally conceived by the Besselsleigh Trust to provide a route for traffic wanting to reach Reading without having to go via Wallingford. This now forms the basis of the modern A417. Along its length several toll houses were constructed. Gates were located at Scotlands Ash near West Hagbourne, opposite the Horse and Harrow public house. Another was located at the top of Chalk Hill in Aston Tirrold. The last gate was just outside Streatley, where the road to the golf course branches off.

In 1858 the work of repealing the Turnpike Acts began with the creation of Sanitary Authorities. Duties for road repair were transferred to local government highways districts. After 1870 there were practically no toll houses left in operation; old gates were torn down and toll houses sold off.

Milestones were set up along most Turnpike Roads. Each milestone marked the distance to major towns. Five or six different styles are used on the local turnpike network and most surviving stones date from the middle of the 19th century. The nearest milestone to Blewburton Hill stands at the top of Blewbury Hill, on the south side of the road almost opposite Blewbury Barn.

STAGECOACH TRAVEL AND HIGHWAYMEN

The quality of roads improved immensely after the introduction of the Turnpike Acts, There were refinements on coach design with sprung frameworks being introduced in 1804. Thoroughbred horses could maintain a faster speed and were changed at staging posts and Inns about every twenty miles. In 1784 John Palmer of Bath, with the help of the Prime Minister, William Pitt the Younger, forced a reluctant post office to carry Royal Mail by coach rather than by rider.

Various firms set up as rivals to try to win contracts in this lucrative trade, and they boasted faster and faster mail delivery times. The first public transport system came into being when mail coaches began to carry fee paying passengers as well as mail. They advertised their routes, leaving at pre-announced times from many towns bound for a variety of destinations.

In 1815 John MacAdam designed a better method of road construction, consisting of a solid roadbed raised above the surrounding ground and covered by a layer of stones no larger than two inches in diameter, topped by further layers of finer stone and gravel each layer being rolled and compressed. Macadam's roads were

© MARIA MORRIS

Dedication

This book is dedicated to the memory of Giles Edward Morris who died as the result of a road accident during the preparation of this book. He loved the area and had walked and savoured most of the ancient routes and pathways he researched so carefully. Above all he was devoted to his family and we are grateful to his wife Maria for helping, in spite of her grief, to complete Giles's article for this book.

twenty feet in width, worthy successors to those of the Romans.

With more rich gentlefolk travelling in coaches, highwaymen, a new breed of criminal, emerged and the risk of robbery increased. One local tale tells that Dick Turpin's favourite hostelry in the area was the George Inn in Wallingford. He would always take the same room at the back, overlooking the courtyard where he left his horse Black Bess saddled and bridled so he could leap from the window of his room and make his getaway.

Robbers and felons were often hanged at strategic crossroads as a warning to others. These crimes and punishments are enshrined in some local place and pub names. Hence the aptly named *Highwayman*, a 16th century coaching inn at Woodcote, and the village of Gallows Tree Common near Reading where the grizzly remains of those committed of capital offences were left on view.

FOOTPATHS

A network of footpaths crisscrossed the villages and countryside like a spider's web. It seems surprising that so many paths could have been needed, until one remembers that people walked everywhere. A slightly shorter route would always have been welcome. These paths and bridleways may be ancient also, for they have changed little from those shown in early maps. Numerous paths run down from the Ridgeway and show centuries of wear, scored across the escarpment into deep 'hollow ways' by the passage of pedestrians and animals, and heavy winter rains.

Although some footpaths were lost in World War II, under the pressure of producing more food, traces of them often still remain as sections of disconnected trackway. A footpath closed within recent memory once ran from Blewbury north east to South Moreton. This was cut in the 1950s and never reopened, since few people now walk to Wallingford and need the short cut. Today footpaths are jealously watched over by keen walkers and have a better chance of survival.

GILES EDWARD MORRIS, BLEWBURY.

FOOTNOTE. FOLLOWING THE SAD AND UNTIMELY DEATH OF GILES MORRIS THIS ARTICLE HAS BEEN COMPLETED FROM NOTES AND OTHER MATERIAL KINDLY SUPPLIED BY GILES'S WIFE MARIA.
ACKNOWLEDGEMENTS
THE CAREFUL WORK OF JUDY BARRADELL-SMITH AND AUDREY LONG IN ASSISTING THE EDITORS WITH THIS ARTICLE IS GRATEFULLY ACKNOWLEDGED.
THE EXTRACT FROM THE MAP OF BERKSHIRE BY JOHN ROCQUE 1761 IS REPRODUCED BY KIND PERMISSION OF THE PUBLISHERS HARRY MARGARY. MARGARY AT WWW.HARRYMARGARY.COM

BUILDING STONE IN LOCAL CHURCHES

Before the era of man-made bricks and tiles, building materials often consisted of timber, lime, mud, and even dung, straw and animal hair, but where practical, the preference was always for local rock. The Blewburton Hill area lies within the Vale of White Horse, surrounded by the chalk hills of the Downs and The Chilterns. These hills, rising to over two hundred metres in places, are composed of Cretaceous chalk, formed 95 to 70 million years ago. It was from these hills that the bulk of the building stone for the churches of Upton, Blewbury, Aston Tirrold and Aston Upthorpe was taken. It was not the chalk itself but the flint within it that provided the rubble core for walls and the exterior faces of the churches of the district. Often regarded as a poor substitute, the flint, being available, was a major component in the construction of some of the most significant buildings in towns and villages.

FLINT

Locally, flint was quarried from the Upper Cretaceous chalk of the Downs as nodules or concretions within the rock. Flint nodules vary in size from as small as a grain of sand, to blocks over two feet across, and come in a variety of shapes from smooth and round to irregular, amoeba-like lumps. When dug straight from the chalk, the flint nodules possess a white coating or cortex. [Plate2]. This is nothing to do with the surrounding chalk; it is a part of the flint itself. On exposure to weather, this coating may take on a pale brown colour as iron oxide and other chemicals are absorbed from the surroundings.

Flint is composed almost entirely of silica. Its origins are still debated, but it is generally thought that the flint beds were formed either at the same time as the

Plate 1: The 15th Century Tower of St.Michael's Church Blewbury; built from "Headington Hard" stone.

chalk, or by fresh ground water percolating through the uplifted chalk during the following Tertiary era.

The flint nodules that were used to build the churches of the Blewburton Hill area have been knapped, or shaped, to achieve a pleasing aesthetic effect. [Plate 2 and 3]. Knapping is a skilled trade, time consuming and producing a lot of waste. Furthermore the impervious, glassy surfaces make it difficult to achieve a good bond, particularly with soft lime mortars but with skill and care in their construction, beautiful flint-faced walls may last many centuries.

IMPORTED STONE

Although flint formed the main bulk of the walls, details around the windows and doors (which required greater strength), and the corners of walls, were built from stone. [Plate 4]. Importing stone, even for such important buildings as churches, was very expensive, requiring many men and animals to transport it over great distances along poorly maintained trading routes.

St Michael's church in Blewbury is the oldest of the four churches in the district and dates back to the eleventh century. The original tower was removed, probably in the fifteenth century when the present tower was built [Plate 1]. The stone, known as Headington Hard, used to build the tower is unlike any stone in any of the other churches. It consists of a fine grained, patchy, weathered to grey,

Plate 2: A simple, but very sound, flint wall made with roughly prepared flints embedded in lime mortar.

Plate 3: A more sophisticated wall, built with knapped flints, in Upton church to give a more pleasing, regular effect.

Plate 4: Imported stones used for important courses and around corners, windows and doors of Aston Upthorpe church.

limestone with shell fragments and coral fossils. Identification of the stone is aided by its characteristic cavernous decay [Plate 5] caused by more rapid weathering of the poorly cemented fills of burrows made by crustaceans. This stone was deposited as soft sediment, 159 to 154 million years ago, in the warm, shallow tropical sea that once covered the area.

The first records of quarrying of Headington Hard date back to 1396-7. Headington quarries supplied much of Oxford's building stone between the fifteenth and eighteenth centuries, but after the beginning of the eighteenth century most of the good stone had been extracted and the quarries began to supply an inferior product. This may explain the resistance of Blewbury church tower to weathering, compared to buildings in Oxford, of the same stone but quarried at a later date.

From the same quarries came another stone known as the Headington freestone [Plate 6]. This was used for the interior and round the doors of all the churches in the district. The freestone was deposited in the same period and under the same environmental conditions as the Headington Hard, but possesses certain qualities that make it more suited to detailed, decorative work. To start with, the freestone has fewer large shell fragments than the Headington Hard, leaving a better surface finish when cut and carved. Also, the clasts or fragments that make up the rock are well sorted, that is, they are all of a similar size, giving the stone a more homogeneous structure. [Plate 6]. These characteristics are all suggestive of good quality freestone - a stone that may be cut freely in any direction without fracture or splitting, the essential qualities of a fine building stone.

The corner stones, the rims of the towers, and the stone surrounding the windows of all the churches in the district are different from the stones described above. Again, this stone has been imported, but this time from as far afield as the Cotswold Hills. The stone comes from within the Great Oolite limestones, probably the Taynton Limestone, formed approximately 164 –167 million years ago. This is the best building stone in the Oxford district and has been worked as freestone since at least the fourteenth century. It was the unrivalled freestone during medieval times and demand for it increased further during the renaissance when architects returned from Europe and

Plate 5: The "Headington Hard". This stone was deposited about 155 million years ago, in the shallow tropical sea that once covered the area. The holes and crevices show where softer material has weathered out of the burrows of ancient crustaceans.

Plate 6: "Headington Freestone". Much more uniform and easier to cut and carve for the finer features.

Plate 7: Oolitic limestone in Blewbury Church. This stone comes from within the "Great Oolite limestones" formed about 165 million years ago. It is the best building stone in the Oxford district and has been worked as freestone since at least the fourteenth century. The angled striations show how the deposits were laid down on sloping sand banks under water.

demanded a change from the provincial English style. It was used in most of Oxford's colleges, and was transported all over the country for use in buildings such as Windsor Castle, Eton College and St. Paul's Cathedral.

Taynton and Barrington quarries, along the Windrush Valley, provided the best source of this stone and must have seen considerable business during their heyday. A quarry worker has documented what it was like to work the quarry at Taynton in the 1500s; "quarrying is no job for the faint-hearted. Whenever I go into the workings, I feel like removing my hat to the men who labour here to produce the finest stone in Britain." Local quarry men were very proud of the quality of stone they were producing. The stone is essentially a cross-bedded, shell-fragmented, oolitic limestone lain down during the Middle Jurassic, about 165 million years ago. It was deposited in a warm, shallow sea environment, on a gently sloping shelf. Characterising the Taynton stone are its ooids and cross-stratification. Ooids are tiny grains of sand or fragments of shell that have been gently rolled around in the lime mud (calcium carbonate) of a shallow tropical sea. As wave action rolls these particles about they accumulate more and more lime mud until they form the tiny spheres known as ooids. The ooids and cross-stratification can be seen clearly in the rim of the tower of Blewbury church. [Plate 7] The cross-stratification is the result of the sediment being laid down not in the horizontal plane, but inclined at angles of up to 30 degrees on the steep-sloping leeward surfaces of

Plate 8: A weathered cornerstone of Blewbury Church with repairs.

underwater sand banks and bars.

Over the years, weathering can have a dramatic effect on the condition of stone. Certain parts of the churches of the Blewburton area have deteriorated over time [Plate 8] and have been subsequently replaced with newer stone. This newer stone is known as Bath Box Ground stone; it began to be used from the seventeenth century onwards. It can be seen as replacement blocks of cornerstone in the churches of the area, and shows characteristic calcite veins [Plate 9].

When canals came into existence at the beginning of the nineteenth century it became convenient to load stone on to barges at Bath, and ship it around the country. By 1870, Bath stone had replaced a high proportion of the earlier worked native Oxfordshire stone throughout the region.

JANE WORRALL, OXFORDSHIRE GEOLOGY TRUST (WWW.OXFORDSHIREGT.ORG)

ALL IMAGES © OXFORDSHIRE GEOLOGY TRUST, DECEMBER 2005 EXCEPT WHERE SHOWN.

© BERNARD MATTIMORE

Plate 9: A window, beautifully repaired with Bath Box Ground Stone

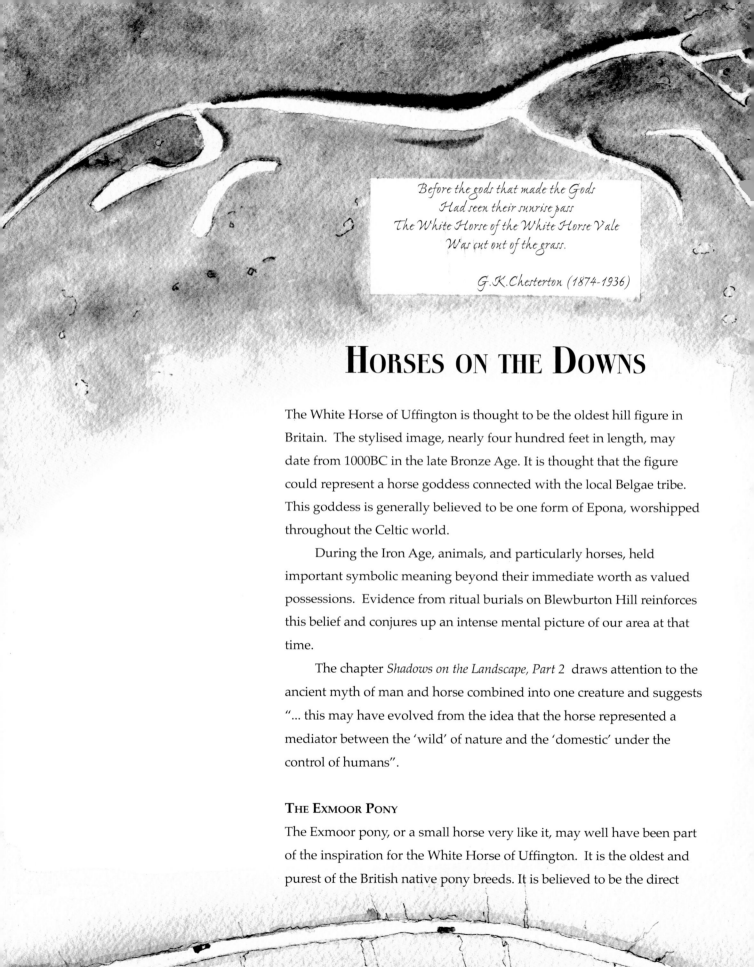

Before the gods that made the Gods
Had seen their sunrise pass
The White Horse of the White Horse Vale
Was cut out of the grass.

G.K.Chesterton (1874-1936)

HORSES ON THE DOWNS

The White Horse of Uffington is thought to be the oldest hill figure in Britain. The stylised image, nearly four hundred feet in length, may date from 1000BC in the late Bronze Age. It is thought that the figure could represent a horse goddess connected with the local Belgae tribe. This goddess is generally believed to be one form of Epona, worshipped throughout the Celtic world.

During the Iron Age, animals, and particularly horses, held important symbolic meaning beyond their immediate worth as valued possessions. Evidence from ritual burials on Blewburton Hill reinforces this belief and conjures up an intense mental picture of our area at that time.

The chapter *Shadows on the Landscape, Part 2* draws attention to the ancient myth of man and horse combined into one creature and suggests "... this may have evolved from the idea that the horse represented a mediator between the 'wild' of nature and the 'domestic' under the control of humans".

THE EXMOOR PONY

The Exmoor pony, or a small horse very like it, may well have been part of the inspiration for the White Horse of Uffington. It is the oldest and purest of the British native pony breeds. It is believed to be the direct descendant of the horses that walked into Britain as the ice retreated. Skeletons from ancient horse burials bear an uncanny similarity to the Exmoor pony of today, showing beyond doubt that they were highly prized and respected, even worshipped, by the Celts.

As one would expect they are strong and tough and well able to look after themselves without human assistance. They stand about eleven to twelve hands high and have a strong stocky frame. They have a double winter coat, one waterproof and the other warm. Hunter-gatherers probably saw them as a food source but later they were tamed and provided immeasurable assistance to the development of farming and transport and a strong and faithful ally to fighting bands and armies over thousands of years.

Able to thrive throughout the year in the open on a diet of very poor quality herbage such as gorse, brambles and moor grass, a small herd of these adorable, now rare, truly wild animals helps to maintain the increasingly scarce lowland heath on Snelsmore Common Country Park near Newbury.

Exmoor ponies on a wet winter's day feeding on gorse. They are uncannily like the Bronze and Iron Age horses found in ritual burial sites.

The Shire horse or "Gentle Giant", descended from "The British War Horse" and "The English Great Horse"

THE SHIRE HORSE OR "GENTLE GIANT"

A rarity now, the Shire horse a century ago was still a primary source of power on roads and farms. The modern Shire horse is thought to have its origins in the English "Great Horse". This,

The English Thoroughbred, originating from just three 17th-century stallions and a hundred "Royal Mares".

Riding for sport and relaxation is an ever-increasing pastime today. This picture was taken on the slopes of Blewburton Hill.

in turn, was a development of the British "War Horse" whose strength, courage and discipline were spoken of with admiration by the chroniclers of the Roman legions when they first landed on British shores.

For many centuries, the whole military effort of England depended upon the ancestors of the Shire horse. For five hundred years, from the reign of Henry II to that of Elizabeth I, constant efforts were made to increase the size and numbers of The Great Horse purely for military purposes. It is recorded that in the early part of this period, King John imported a hundred stallions from Holland and the Low Countries to enhance the strain. During the reign of Henry VIII laws were passed forbidding the use of horses of less than fifteen hands in height for breeding purposes. The export of horses, even to Scotland, was prohibited.

In both war and peacetime England depended upon the muscular strength of tens of thousands of horses, large and small, to move the commerce of the nation over appalling roads and to power every farm in the land. There was no shortage of demand for ever-heavier animals of prodigious strength and faithful obedience. The magnificent Shire horse was the result.

THOROUGHBREDS AND THE GALLOPS

The firm, even turf of the Berkshire Downs provides one of the best training grounds for racehorses in the country. For the same reasons men and horses were trained here for cavalry regiments in great numbers. The wide, sweeping strips of turf called "The Gallops" now criss-cross the landscape once grazed by tens of thousands of sheep.

The old English chronicles mention that horse racing was an ancient, national tradition of the Anglo-Saxons. By the eleventh century racing was organized and controlled according to certain rules; races were conducted over long distances and owners of winning animals received honorary rewards but there were no money prizes.

English Knights, returning from the Crusades in the twelfth century, brought Arab horses back and bred them with English horses to improve their speed.

Charles II (1660 to 1685) held the first race meetings in Britain at Newmarket. He also imported horses that were to enter the pedigrees of the English Thoroughbred. Today's thoroughbreds all originate from just three stallions, imported around the end of the 17th century: The Byerley Turk, Darley Arabian and Godolphin Barb, and less than a hundred mares, now known as the "Royal Mares".

Fourteen to seventeen hands high, the Thoroughbred of today, is defined as having "a spirited and bold temperament with refined head, long neck, sloping shoulders, deep body, muscular hindquarters and fine long legs". They became a very familiar sight in Blewbury and Aston in the early twentieth century, when many racing stables were developed in both villages, as well as on the Downs themselves.

One of the most famous names associated with racing in Blewbury is Dick Francis. A veteran bomber pilot during the war he was a professional jockey from 1948 to 1957. He rode for the Queen Mother for four seasons and was Champion Jockey in 1954. A world famous event in his life occurred in the Grand National of 1956 when his mount, Devon Loch, collapsed fifty yards from the winning post when ten lengths in front. By 1967 he had become the *Sunday Express* Racing Correspondent and, with much help from his wife Mary, a highly successful writer of thriller novels, invariably set in the racing world.

PETER COCKRELL

POEM © ESTATE OF JOHN BETJEMAN; PHOTO © BERNARD MATTIMORE

... To the Down the string of horses moving out of sight and mind ...

From the poem Upper Lambourne

ACKNOWLEDGEMENTS
HELP WITH THE FOLLOWING PICTURES IS GRATEFULLY ACKNOWLEDGED: SHIRE HORSES - ADAM HENSON OF COTSWOLD FARM PARK; EXMOOR PONIES - KEITH TOMEY, COUNTRYSIDE RANGER SNELSMORE COMMON; THOROUGHBREDS - MR & MRS AND EVE JOHNSON-HOUGHTON OF WOODWAY STABLES AND GERARD BUTLER OF CHURN STABLES. THE EXCERPT FROM JOHN BETJEMAN'S POEM IS REPRODUCED BY KIND PERMISSION OF JOHN MURRAY PUBLISHERS.

REFERENCE: BLEWBURY SELF PORTRAIT. 1967

TRACES OF THE PAST

© PETER COCKRELL

*Twin Bronze Age barrows on
Churn Down*

Professional archaeologists have
investigated Blewburton, and the
area surrounding it, on numerous
occasions over the past century.
Their conclusions, and some of
the objects they have found, are
described elsewhere in this book.
However, they are not the only
ones to have taken an interest
in the past of the chalk downs
and the villages at their foot. For
more than a hundred and fifty
years, local people have sought
to understand the history of this
region from the objects left behind in the ground.

VICTORIAN DISCOVERIES

In 1845 one of the Blewbury Lousleys, and his friend Jesse King,
opened the northern one of the twin barrows still very visible on
Churn Down. They found an arrowhead and fragments of a black urn;
sometime after they left their "dig", the side collapsed, exposing "many
small vessels of British pottery, which seemed to have been set in a
circle". No trace of these survives.

Three years later, antiquarian Rev.Dr John Wilson, of Trinity
College, Oxford, dug into a number of tumuli on the downs, including
the other of the twin barrows. He found the cremated bones of a
woman and a child, and a bronze dagger with two rivets where the
handle had been, identified as Early Bronze Age. It was given to the
Ashmolean Museum.

Towards the end of the century, Eli Caudwell, of Ashbrook farm in
Blewbury, found an ancient axe in the stream bed in his garden. He lent
it to Reading Museum where it was identified as a Saxon battle-axe.

A century later it has not been easy to trace these objects. Steve

Russell visited both the Reading and Oxford Museums, and made endless enquiries of museum authorities both nearby and further afield. No one could find any sign of either object. However, from illustrations of a similar axe, the Reading Museum curator suggested that it resembled pictures of carpenters' axes in the Bayeux tapestry. It seems more likely that Blewbury would have produced a carpenter's axe than "an exceptionally large battle axe". And after long searches into the, by then (2005) packaged, Ashmolean collections, an impressively diligent curator finally located the whereabouts of the bronze dagger.

Woodmen and a carpenter working with axes, from the Victorian Replica of the Bayeux Tapestry at the Museum of Reading.

RECENT FINDS

In the mid-20th century, metal detectors were developed from techniques used to locate land mines. Gradually the craze caught on and metal detecting became the hobby, indeed the passion, of dedicated individuals throughout the country. Not content with the simple treasure hunting aspect of the pastime, enthusiasts published specialist journals, and detailed catalogues of all categories of metal objects were produced. Museum staff were willing to help identify the more unusual finds. Metal detecting fans could be as happy at home, poring over books in comfort, as they were tramping over recently ploughed fields in the autumn chill.

Their metal detectors pick up small metal objects, such as coins, in the top six to eight inches of the soil, and larger objects down to eighteen inches or so. Deep ploughing churns up the top layers of soil so that objects rarely lie exactly where they were lost but they still evoke an unbroken thread of everyday life from Celtic times to the present day. They are a touching record of the minutiae of daily existence in a country village. Most common of all are the coins, especially Roman coins, which

Roman coins are found in great numbers in the area.

Roman silver coins (clockwise from bottom left): Emperors Septimus Severus, 193-211AD; Antonius Pius, 138-161; Elagabalus, 218-222; Valentinian I, 364-375

(Top) Edward I coin; a Saxon silver sceat 675-690; and a silver half-penny of Edward the Confessor 1042-1066.

have been found in their hundreds. Following them, coins from Saxon times are far rarer, but an unusual, later Saxon sceat has been picked up in the parish, as well as coins of nearly all the crowned heads of England from the Norman conquest onwards. We are not careful with our cash. A recent trawl of the Blewbury Play Close with a metal detector brought to light a handful of coins: some ten pounds worth of present-day currency! The oldest coins found in the parish, however, were Celtic, ranging from 20 BC to 5 AD.

HOME LIFE

Jewellery, buckles, buttons, and belt strap ends have been made of metal since early times. These items make up a substantial part of the collections of owners of metal detectors, and they also show the longest and most consistent usage. A fine Celtic brooch, in perfect condition and dating to around 100 BC, was found between Aston and Cholsey by one of the veteran enthusiasts. Several slightly later Celtic brooches, and many Roman ones, have been unearthed in this area. They are a reminder that the safety pin, rather more decorative then than now, was worn when Blewburton hillfort was in use. Later brooches and buckles, from all periods, are scattered across the fields around the villages. Very little is found within the villages themselves; objects lost there were presumably picked up again later, whereas something lost during work in the fields was lost for good. Or almost.

Among the more unexpected items from later centuries are the lead skirt weights with which Victorian ladies kept their crinolines (or simpler gowns) decently around their ankles. Then there are the shoe pattens, the villager's reply to muddy tracks and fields before the Wellington boot was invented. The ingenious patten consisted of a metal band, set on end and curved into a circle, on the upper side of which were lugs and a small wooden platform, which allowed it to be strapped under the shoe. It was England's answer to the wooden clog.

Work at home was always part of women's life in the past, and their spindle whorls and thimbles have been picked up in great numbers by the detectors. It is interesting to see the development of metal thimbles over the centuries, from simple finger bands in the 14th and 15th centuries to a beehive shape and finally to the shape we know

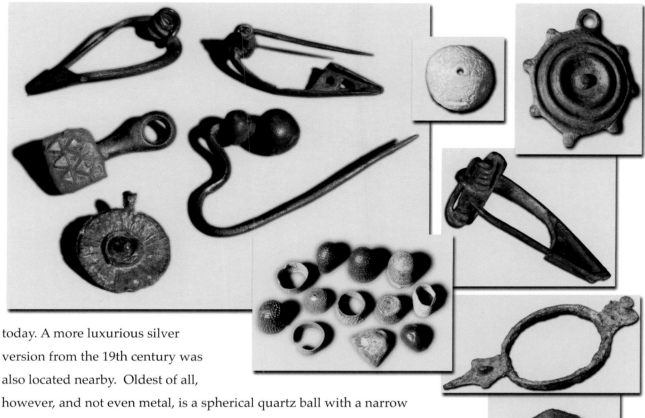

today. A more luxurious silver version from the 19th century was also located nearby. Oldest of all, however, and not even metal, is a spherical quartz ball with a narrow hole bored part way into it, thought to be a tool for pushing a large needle through hide and made, perhaps, as long ago as 4,000 BC.

Home was a place for enjoyment as well though: children's toys sometimes come to light, little horses made of lead and canons of bronze. A lead dice of Roman times shows this as a favoured metal for such pursuits. Clay pipe stems, and also occasionally pipe bowls, are picked up in most gardens, as well as out in the fields while metal detecting.

LIFE AT WORK

Many of the objects found by metal detectors relate directly to farm work and some date back to Saxon times. One of the earliest tools found recently is a magnificent later Bronze Age socketed axe head, picked out by metal detector in the fields below Blewburton Hill. One of the most notable finds, by another of Blewbury's veteran collectors, is an Anglo Saxon stirrup strap mount in perfect condition, which has been dated to the late 10th or early 11th century. Other clear Saxon stirrup mounts, ranging from the 8th to the 11th centuries have been

(Clockwise from top left): a group of Celtic brooches, 1st Century BC; prehistoric quartz ball, thought to have served as a thimble; Roman disc brooch, 2nd Century AD; Roman brooch; shoe patten, to raise foot above the mud; Roman lead dice; and a collection of thimbles from various periods.

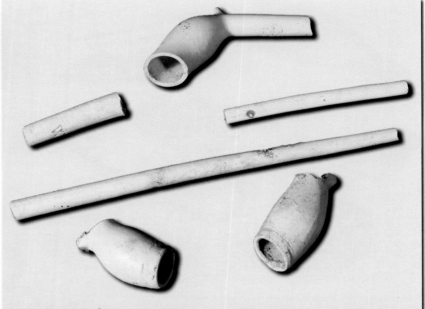

found, as well as several Saxon strap ends.

Horses and other animals were adorned with round crotal bells in the 17th and 18th centuries and many of these have been found in the fields, as have many of the horse brasses, which adorned the great shire horses.

At the other end of the time scale, the same collector found a fine horse brass, which he was able to identify as the very one shown in a photograph of 1892, of Eli Caudwell with his carthorse. Traces of the commerce of the countryside may be less common than those of the farm work, but nevertheless they do also appear in the fields. Lead weights are not uncommon and there are even some small weights for checking gold coins. Seals were widely used in medieval times to mark a trader's goods, and many of these have been found; traders

(Clockwise from top left): Bronze Age socketed axe head; clay pipes and pipe stems; Eli Cauldwell horse brass; Saxon strap end, circa 1000 AD; crotal bells 17th and 18th century; Saxon stirrup strap mount, circa 1000 AD.

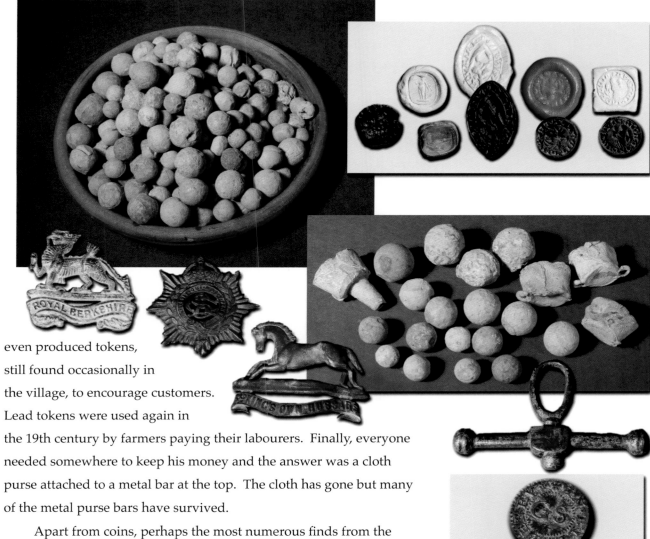

even produced tokens,
still found occasionally in
the village, to encourage customers.
Lead tokens were used again in
the 19th century by farmers paying their labourers. Finally, everyone
needed somewhere to keep his money and the answer was a cloth
purse attached to a metal bar at the top. The cloth has gone but many
of the metal purse bars have survived.

Apart from coins, perhaps the most numerous finds from the
fields around Blewbury have been lead musket balls. Of course,
Blewburton was built for defensive purposes, but since then, we
like to think, this has for the most part been a peaceable part of the
world. Not so, it would seem, from the prevalence of musket balls in
the fields to the west of the village. Many, the larger ones, date from
the time of the Civil War. Not infrequently they show signs of having
been chewed, to render them more lethal. They are often accompanied
by small lead containers, cup or funnel shaped, from which the
gunpowder was measured into the musket. Smaller musket balls came
later, and could have been used against deer or other game. From later
times, also, come numerous military badges: one collector has badges
of the Oxford and Bucks, the Royal Berks, and the 3rd King's Own

*(Clockwise from top left): musket
balls dating from Civil War to later
period; 12th-13th century seals
and impressions; musket balls and
gunpowder measures; metal purse
bar; token of George Stanton, mercer
of Blewbury, 1660; badges of 3rd
King's Own Hussars, Oxford and
Bucks and Royal Berks regiments.*

Hussars regiments.

Finally, there are even traces of the religious life of the villagers. The Roman temple on Lowbury Hill has been well excavated, but examples of Roman votive offerings, in the shape of miniature axes, have been found closer to the village of Blewbury. A splendid little bronze figurine of a winged boy, thought to be Roman, might also have been an offering. From later times, a metal pilgrim's badge of the 12th to 15th centuries has been found, as well as a number of lead ampullae (of a similar period) in which holy water was carried.

For a district with a past dating back to the end of the Bronze Age, and a central village, Blewbury, which was already described as "venerable" over a thousand years ago, this may not seem a great treasure trove. No spectacular hordes of coins, or ancient tools, or jewellery, have been found here. However, the small objects painstakingly extracted from the fields, and cleaned and identified by enthusiastic collectors, build up an appealing picture of the everyday life of a typical village of the chalk downs of southern England.

SHIRLEY KAY AND STEVE RUSSELL
(SHIRLEY KAY IS AUTHOR OF FIFTEEN BOOKS ON THE MIDDLE EAST AND OTHER WORKS.)

ACKNOWLEDGEMENTS.
ALL EXCEPT TWO OF THE ARTEFACTS SHOWN WERE KINDLY LENT BY ALAN GEORGE AND CYRIL GODWIN WHOSE HELP WITH SELECTING, IDENTIFYING AND PHOTOGRAPHING THE OBJECTS FROM THEIR COLLECTIONS IS GRATEFULLY ACKNOWLEDGED. THE BRONZE AGE AXE WAS VERY KINDLY LENT BY THE FINDER GARY HORN. THE CLAY PIPES WERE FROM THE COLLECTION OF PETER COCKRELL.

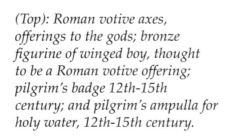

(Top): Roman votive axes, offerings to the gods; bronze figurine of winged boy, thought to be a Roman votive offering; pilgrim's badge 12th-15th century; and pilgrim's ampulla for holy water, 12th-15th century.

THE EVOLUTION OF HORSESHOES

Old horseshoes are a fascinating and common find made by metal detector in fields, gardens and old roadways around Blewbury. Just three collections have produced examples running from the 10th to the 20th centuries. The patterns of shoes, nails and nail holes have changed only slowly so that dates can be roughly estimated. The examples are shown at one-third actual size.

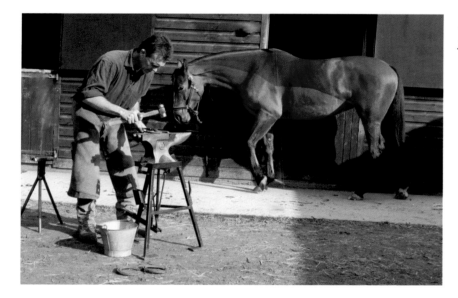

Ian Belcher, third generation farrier, at work in Blewbury 2006.

The age-old method of "Hot shoeing" still in use.

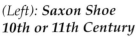

(Left): **Saxon Shoe 10th or 11th Century**
Shoes from this period had a distinctive wavy rim caused by driving a spike through the red-hot iron to form six countersunk nail holes. They may also have an early "calkin" (thickened heel) to improve grip or correct gait.

(Right): **Guildhall Shoe 13th Century**
The typical "Guildhall" shoe, with its asymmetric shape, pointed arch and narrow inner branch, was in use during the 13th, 14th and 15th centuries. This one has two calkins. A dating feature among Guildhall shoes is the use of the spiked or "frosty" nail to steady the horse in icy conditions during the second half of the 13th Century.

(Above): **Norman Shoe 11th or 12th Century**
Still with a slightly wavy rim and six square nail holes. The wavy rim had disappeared completely by around 1300. Shoe manufacture was now a major industry. In the reign of Richard I, 1157-99, over fifty thousand horseshoes were required for the crusades alone.

(Left): **Dove Shoe 15th Century**
The symmetric, smoothly curved Dove shoe was named after the river Dove in Staffordshire where an example was found with the precise date of 1322. Our example is thought to date from about 1450 with one calkin. Both the Dove and the Guildhall forms come from a period when shoes and shoeing had become a form of tax. For example the king could, and did, hold landowners to deliver specified numbers of men and horses with shoes or iron for making shoes.

(Right): **Keyhole Shoe 17th Century**
Shoes in this group, with the very distinctive "keyhole" inner shape, date from the 17th to the 19th century. They tend to be much larger and heavier than previous forms with more nails. This example is well worn but still shows a "fullered" groove around the shoe to protect the nail heads.

(Above): **Keyhole Shoe 18th Century**
This is an immense example weighing 44 ounces, clearly for a heavy draught horse. It also shows the "dished" form of this type where the hoof was rounded downwards in the middle or "frog" of the horse's foot. The basic keyhole shape varied considerably during the period.

(Left): **Tongue Shoe
18th Century**
Partly contemporary with keyhole types. It was probably used more for riding horses than draught horses. It gets its name from the inner "tongue" shape. The branches are very much wider apart than the keyhole type. This example has simple, bent calkins.

(Above): **Saddle Horse or Hunter Shoe, mid 19th Century**
Clips were used in all types of shoe except racing at this time. It was a period of experimentation and shoes for saddle horses and hunters became very light in weight.

(Right): **Heavy Draught Horse 19th Century**
By now most shoes were made from a strip of wrought iron with varying length of heel, both shorter and longer than the hoof. The nails were placed at the sides avoiding the front and rear of the foot. This example can be dated after 1800 due to the toe clip and later than 1864 due to the stamped out and tapered nail holes.

(Left): **Racing Plate 20th Century**
Made of light alloy and deeply fullered (grooved) to protect the nail heads. The large number of nail-holes would not all be used at the same time.

(Right): **Donkey Shoe**
Similar to horse shoes but generally smaller and longer in proportion to width.

(Above): **Ox Shoe
Date unknown**
The shoeing of oxen dates from the 11th Century. Two were required on each foot: one for each claw of the cloven hoof. They were made of much thinner metal than horseshoes and have rusted away more readily so fewer are found.

(Right): **Mule Shoe**
Date unknown
The long pointed heels usually distinguish mule shoes from all others. They were frequently driven into gateposts to serve as catches after their primary purpose was fulfilled.

(Right): **Roman Hippo-Sandal**
Nearly 2000 years old this is a (crushed) iron, temporary Roman horseshoe. It was strapped to the hoof rather than nailed.

(Photograph taken by kind permission of Oxfordshire County Museum Service)

PETER COCKRELL

ACKNOWLEDGEMENTS
THE EXAMPLES ARE FROM THE COLLECTIONS OF ERIC RICHARDSON, MATT KNAPPER AND CYRIL GODWIN. ALL IMAGES IN THIS ARTICLE ARE © BERNARD MATTIMORE

REFERENCE
SHIRE ALBUM 19, *OLD HORSESHOES* BY IVAN G. SPARKES

OUR CHANGING CLIMATE

Recent experience has shown that weather changes dramatically from day to day, as well as over longer periods of time. Extreme conditions stick in our minds. For example, the recent summer of 2003 was very hot and dry. Plants, even trees, died in this area through lack of rain and people died of heat stroke in France. The months of December 2001 and January 2002, on the contrary, were exceptionally wet, with rainfall in these two months exceeding an average year's rainfall for Blewbury.

In the winter of 1981/2 temperatures in Blewbury dropped to minus 18°C. For four days snow and ice prevented movement by road in or out of the village. A prolonged power cut meant no piped water, no heating, and little food. It certainly felt like a return to harsher times. Imagine living on Blewburton Hill in these conditions. There would have been no pubs doing a roaring trade, with wood fires, a supply of food in the freezer and a good supply of beer as there were in 81/82.

The concept of short-term climatic variation is familiar to all of us. What is perhaps less well known is how much our climate has changed over the recent and more distant past. Most historical knowledge of climatic change takes the form of anecdotes or human recollections such as the Thames freezing over in London during the 1600s or the "Little Ice Age", as it is often called. The problem is that weather records such as temperature, wind speed, rainfall and pressures, have only been

Cumulus sky over the Downs.

kept for three to four hundred years. Records for Southern Britain go back to 1659 and Oxford University (only twelve miles from Blewbury) has a record that goes back to 1767.

In order to infer climatic change before these dates, it is necessary to use other measurements that can be related to temperature. Tree rings, for example, can provide a record,

© PETER COCKRELL

TIME Millions of Years Before Present	Average Global Temperature		
	Period	Present Cooler	Warmer
0	Quarternary		
1.67	Pliocene		
5.1			
	Miocene		
24			
36	Oligocene		
	Eccene		
55	Paleocene		
65			
	Cretaceous		
140			
	Jurassic		
210			
	Triassic		
250			
290	Permian		
	Carboniferous		
360	Devonian		
410			
	Silurian		

Figure 1. Temperature change over Geological Time (adapted from Valdes et al., 1999)

because the growth of a tree depends on having warm temperatures and moist conditions. Also the ice cores from Greenland and pollen and sediment records from lakes and the seas around Britain can give us indications of temperature change. These cores can be sliced up, dated and measurements of isotopes of oxygen taken. These measurements can then be related to temperature to give a time series going back thousands of years, as indicated in Figures 1 and 2.

So, what has happened in Blewbury in the past? Figure 1 shows the changes over geological time and, as can be seen, temperatures have varied enormously with warm almost tropical conditions in the Cretaceous and Jurassic (Dinosaur times) and a freezing, snowball existence in the Permian period. During the Quaternary, the landmass that would become the British Isles witnessed frequent and often dramatic transformations in climate, environment and landscape. The long (and often short) term effects of these factors on human populations must have been dramatic if not catastrophic.

ICE AGES

Ice sheets repeatedly advanced and retreated, fluctuating global sea levels led to sporadic isolation from mainland Europe, and major changes in the pattern of North Atlantic currents dramatically influenced the nature and rapidity of climate change. Repeated glaciation successively remodelled the British landscape and its river systems. Diverse mammalian fauna have been recorded from this period, with species as different as hippopotamus and reindeer. While the flora varied from temperate woodland to steppe tundra.

Against this background, a fluctuating signal of human presence can be recognised over at least half a million years. Abundant archaeology has been preserved at many British sites and faunal remains provide further direct evidence of human activity in the form of butchered or modified bones. These are often found associated on well-preserved occupation surfaces, a rare occurrence in a European context. Although actual human fossils are rare in Britain, those that do occur have been extensively studied. Hence there are few better places to examine the many factors influencing and limiting the distribution of early human populations.

During the peak of the last Ice Age, 20,000 years ago, the northern polar front extended down to the level of Spain and there were icebergs floating off the coast of Portugal. Britain was locked in an icy grip and during the winter was surrounded by frozen seas. It is thought that people were unable to live in Britain during this period. At the times of the lowest sea levels and maximum ice, the continental shelf on which Britain is situated was joined by quite an extensive land bridge to Europe. So people, animals and plants were able, periodically, to spread from Europe. But when sea levels were high, Britain was either an island or connected to the continent by only a very narrow land bridge. The interaction of these forces can be modelled and so the ability of plants, animals and people to come to and fro can be charted. Thus, as the climate pendulum swung backwards and forwards, profound climatic and geographic changes occurred. However, the period of interest to Blewbury with regard to human occupation is really the Holocene: the time since the last ice age.

Figure 2. Temperature and Vegetation Change over the Holocene (adapted from Newsom and Hanwell , 1982).

A BETTER CLIMATE

During the past 13,000 years, the climate in this area has recovered from a very cold state at the end of the last ice age to our relatively balmy conditions now. However, it has not been a smooth transition, as shown in Figure 2. There have been periods of extreme cold immediately after the end of the last ice age and, more recently, in the "Little Ice Age". There were also periods when the climate was warmer than it is now. Distinct changes in tree cover, linked to climate change, occurred as the sub-arctic conditions receded. Open woodland of Silver Birch and pine – as might see in Northern Scandinavia – would have existed around the area at this time, but gradually, denser forests of Oak and Ash competed better than these earlier colonisers as the climate became less cold. Temperatures reached their highest levels around 5,500 BC and this period corresponds to the development of agriculture and the beginning of the Neolithic Age. As the Neolithic Age moved into the Bronze Age, the climate became progressively drier, while the following Iron Age was significantly wetter and cooler.

So how would the climate have affected population development in the area? From 11,000 – 9,500 BC it is likely that the first human

Very clear annual rings in an oak tree. The space between the rings gives an indication of growing conditions for each year.

populations moved into Southern England from continental Europe; human remains for this period have been found in the caves at Cheddar Gorge. Around 10,500 BC a sharp downturn in temperature, known as the Younger Dryas, occurred (see Figure 2). The 15°C drop in winter temperatures would certainly have made living, at a place like Blewburton Hill, impossible. The climate remained very cold until about 8,000 BC and then became warmer and more stable.

The sustained rise in temperature and consequent ice-melt caused a rise in sea level; in about 6,000 BC Britain became an island. At this stage, the Blewbury area may have started to be inhabited as there is evidence of stone age flints in southern Britain, as well as domesticated dogs and a wider range of animal and vegetable foods. As the climate warmed from 6000 to 4000 BC it reached a peak, known as the "Climatic Optimum" with higher temperatures than the 1960s, and rainfall spread evenly throughout the year. The development of stone circles such as Stonehenge and Avebury suggest that celestial events were of great importance, implying that this was a period of clear skies.

It is almost certain that people were living in the Blewbury area by this time, as there was a move from hunting and gathering to a more settled farm-based existence with many pottery finds and sophisticated tools in Southern Britain. The climate during the period 3000-900 BC stabilised and, if anything, started to cool slightly with evidence of reduced rainfall. Temperatures remained high enough for village farming and the occupation of Blewburton Hill. The dawning of the Iron Age was climatically warm and dry in this area, but it was getting wetter and cooler in the North and West of the UK. Peat bogs grew rapidly in mid-Wales and North West England and there was increased storminess and extremes of temperature.

The cooling of the climate in 400-200 BC brought frosty winters, increased wetness and increased storminess during this period. As the Romans arrived, the climate started to warm up again, becoming drier, but there was still enough rainfall to ensure good crops for the rich agriculture of this golden period in Celtic Britain. Over the next 1200 years, the climate remained fairly stable, although there is evidence of cool, wet periods in the 5th and 7th century AD, and there were some bitterly cold winters in the 8th century AD. The period of the early

Middle Ages is thought to have been warm with dry summers and mild winters, probably very similar to our present weather. This would have been a good time to live in this area.

Unfortunately, as shown in Figure 3, the climate deteriorated into the Little Ice Age after the 14th century AD, with significantly lower temperatures and many harsh winters. The population was also afflicted by political upheaval at this time with the plague

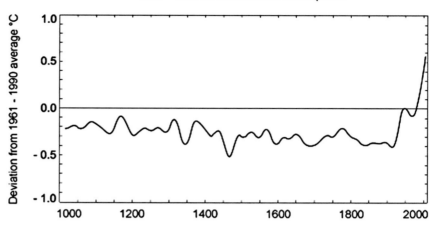

certainly affecting the area in the mid-14th century and repeatedly thereafter. The Little Ice Age extended to 1700 but temperatures started to rise after that, reaching current levels by the mid 19th century. Since then the climate has remained fairly stable, although the recent run of mild winters and warm summers suggests that our climate is changing again. This is highly likely to be man-induced, as carbon dioxide levels in the atmosphere have risen, giving us the well-known "greenhouse" effect. So it looks as though we are heading back to the climatic optimum of 5500 BC when the temperatures were high enough to encourage the first human settlement in the Blewbury area. Also, we may have wetter winters and dryer summers in the future so this would give rise to greater fluctuations in the Blewbury streams and ponds as climate change progresses over the years to come.

Figure 3: Dramatic illustration of man-induced global temperature rise over the last 120 years. Adapted from IPCC, 2001 Report.

PROFESSOR PAUL WHITEHEAD
UNIVERSITY OF READING, SCHOOL OF HUMAN AND ENVIRONMENTAL SCIENCES

REFERENCES
1. BRIFFA, K.R. (2000) ANNUAL CLIMATE VARIABILITY IN THE HOLOCENE: INTERPRETING THE MESSAGE OF ANCIENT TREES, QUATERNARY SCIENCE REVIEW, 19, 87-105; 2. HULME, M. AND BARROW, E. (1997) CLIMATE OF THE BRITISH ISLES: PRESENT, PAST AND FUTURE, ROUTLEDGE, LONDON; 3. LIMBRICK KJ, WHITEHEAD PG, BUTTERFIELD D, REYNARD N. (2000) ASSESSING THE POTENTIAL IMPACT OF CLIMATE CHANGE SCENARIOS ON THE HYDROLOGICAL REGIME OF THE RIVER KENNET AT THEALE, BERKSHIRE, SOUTH-CENTRAL ENGLAND, UK: AN APPLICATION AND EVALUATION OF THE NEW SEMI-DISTRIBUTED MODEL, INCA. SCI TOTAL ENVIRON 252, 539-556; 4. MITHEN, S.J. (2003) AFTER THE ICE, ORION BOOKS, LONDON; 5. NEWSON, M.D. AND HANWELL, J.D. (1982) SYSTEMATIC PHYSICAL GEOGRAPHY, MACMILLAN EDUCATION, HAMPSHIRE; 6. ROBERTS, N. (1998) THE HOLOCENE: AN ENVIRONMENTAL HISTORY, BLACKWELL, OXFORD; 7. VALDES, P.J., SPICER, R.A., SELLWOOD, B.W., PALMER, D.C. (1999) UNDERSTANDING PAST CLIMATES: MODELLING ANCIENT WEATHER, INTERACTIVE CD, OVERSEAS PUBLISHERS ASSOCIATION AMSTERDAM BV.

PART II
AN ANCIENT LANDSCAPE

Up on the Downs

Up on the Downs the red-eyed kestrels hover,
Eyeing the grass.
The field-mouse flits like a shadow into cover
As their shadows pass.

Men are burning the gorse on the down's shoulder;
A drift of smoke
Glitters with fire and hangs, and the skies smoulder,
And the lungs choke.

Once the tribe did thus on the down, on these downs burning
Men in the frame,
Crying to the gods of the downs till their brains were turning
And the gods came.

And today on the downs, in the wind, the hawks, the grasses,
In blood and air,
Something passes me and cries as it passes,
On the chalk downland bare.

John Masefield (1878-1967)

John Masefield wrote this poem at Lollingdon Farm near
Aston Tirrold in 1916/17

FROM CAMP SITES TO SETTLEMENTS
THE MESOLITHIC TO THE BRONZE AGE

When the last Ice Age came to an end 10,000 years ago and the ice sheet that had covered northern Britain receded, bands of people walked from northern France into southern England. They brought with them tens of thousands of years of experience that would enable them to thrive in this slowly changing environment. The zone was dominated at first by birch and pine trees and then, a couple of thousand years later, by the spread northward of broad-leaved plants such as elm and oak. About 8,500 years ago, when rising sea levels cut Britain off from the Continent, the landscape around Blewburton Hill was covered with the mixed woodland we see today. The river valleys provided the pioneers with the easiest routes for long distance travel as they sought out new regions to exploit; the Thames valley and that of its tributary, the Kennet, on the other side of the Berkshire Downs from Blewburton Hill, became important thoroughfares. The people of this period, which is known as the Mesolithic, lived a highly mobile lifestyle that was largely governed by the patterns of the seasons, following and hunting their main prey of red deer, roe deer, wild pig and aurochs, a wild ox now extinct. The forest provided both cover for their hunting and, at the woodland margins, swathes of hazel trees whose nutshells are often found in abundance on Mesolithic sites.

MESOLITHIC SKILLS

Mesolithic hunter-gatherers did not leave a strong imprint on the landscape. At Goring, an important river crossing for prey animals, and at North Stoke, families established camps that are detectable now only by the signs of flint working. No remains of dwellings have been found there, and it is likely that their shelters were lightly constructed and probably not intended to be permanent. From these camps at the side of the Thames, the heavily wooded downlands beyond Streatley were roamed extensively, since we can see that the scatters of flint

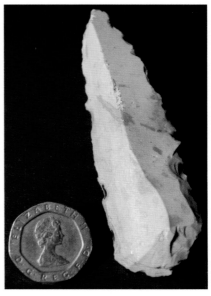

© BERNARD MATTIMORE

An elegant flint end scraper about 7.5 cm long, probably from the Early Mesolithic around 10,000 years ago. The thicker end is prepared for use by the removal of small flakes to form a durable edge, a process known as "retouching". Found near The Cleve in Blewbury and kindly lent by June Smith.

A Mesolithic hunter-gatherer camp by the Thames near the Goring Gap about 9,000 years ago. This band of about twenty-five people is shown preparing and using tools, hunting weapons, clothing and shelter made from raw materials from plants and animals. The organic artefacts have disappeared from the archaeological evidence, leaving only the worked flint from tools and weapons.

weapons and tools are spread thinly but evenly over wide areas. Flint was vital to the Mesolithic folk, who raised the technology of stone tool-making to its zenith, producing arrows and spears tipped with rows of small, delicately worked pieces known as microliths, as well as long finely-wrought flint blades. The people who visited and revisited Windmill Hill at Nettlebed towards the end of the Mesolithic period, to make and re-make flint tools in large quantities, were providing the technology that underpinned a way of life that perfectly exploited the richness of the landscape. Yet in the 4,000 years of the Mesolithic

© RICHARD HOOK

WAYLAND'S SMITHY

Beside the Ridgeway and only a short distance from White Horse Hill lies the Neolithic burial mound known as Wayland's Smithy. This impressive monument must have been well known to the people of this area throughout the 5500 years since the tomb was built. There were two clear stages of construction. First a wooden chamber for about fifteen people was covered with chalk and edged with huge stone slabs. The removal of the chalk left a deep surrounding ditch. Two centuries later, a much larger tomb was built completely covering the first with flanking ditches along the whole length. This had three stone lined burial chambers, which may have been used for several hundred years before being sealed. It is thought to have been a ceremonial site where the living and the dead were linked. It may also have marked the community's ownership of the surrounding land.

The Saxons, four thousand years later, believed that the tomb was created by one of their gods, Wayland the Smith. The legend grew that Wayland would re-shoe the horse of any passing traveller who left a silver penny beside the tomb. Hence the name we know today.

The chambers were opened in 1920 and, even though they had been ransacked, they still contained the jumbled remains of at least eight people.

PETER COCKRELL

(Top): Wayland's Smithy, 5500 years old, a ceremonial site where the living and the dead were linked. (Below): the entrance to the tomb at Wayland's Smithy

PHOTOGRAPH: © BERNARD MATTIMORE. INFORMATION COURTESY OF ENGLISH HERITAGE

period, they left not one visible mark or monument.

Towards the end of the Mesolithic, around 7,000 years ago, life was starting to alter in the area around Blewburton Hill. Archaeologists have noted subtle changes to shapes of microliths, such as those found on the higher ground near Cholsey. Flint tranchet axes for felling trees also appeared, like the one found at Churn on Blewbury Down. Clearings had been made in woodland before, but only as killing zones for hunting. Now the methodical clearing of land for other purposes began. One of these was to provide a setting for the first two types of

© BARNARD MATTIMORE

Mesolithic flint cores from Gatehampton Farm, near Goring, showing the flake scars left where flakes were struck from the core, kindly lent by Philip Turner.

A Mesolithic hunter making projectiles tipped with rows of microliths.

This perfect and exquisitely worked flint, projectile point, of a style known as "leaf arrowhead", about 2.5 cm long, is typical of those made in the Early Neolithic, about 5,500 years ago. Found close to Blewburton Hill and kindly lent by Gary Horn.

monument to be created in the area, marking the start of mankind's permanent alteration of the landscape. This heralded the beginning of the Neolithic era, when people first started to make pottery.

THE NEOLITHIC AGE

On Blewbury Down, just below the racing gallops east of Churn Farm, a long mound stood for some 6,000 years, until it was ploughed out during the 20th Century. This massive tomb, over forty metres long and about twenty metres wide, was constructed from the turf, soil and chalk that surrounded it, a process that left flanking ditches as an integral part of the monument. Known as "long barrows", these imposing tombs, shining white in the evening sunlight were not, as one might expect, the last resting place of single powerful individuals. Instead they held the bones of many men, women and children, not as whole skeletons, but as venerated and carefully selected bones piled up inside stone or timber chambers within the mounds. It is thought that these tombs, such as the famous Wayland's Smithy, thirty-two kilometres to the west along the Ridgeway, acted as markers of identity for extended family groups or tribes. The long barrows are often within a few kilometres of the other type of monument that Early Neolithic people first built 6,000 year ago – the causewayed enclosure, the most famous example of which is on Windmill Hill near Avebury. These consist of single or roughly concentric circular ditches and banks, with the ditches built in sections with gaps in between. During the excavation on Blewburton Hill in 1967, a short ditch segment was found a few metres in from the entrance to the Iron Age earthwork. It contained Early Neolithic objects, including a polished axe from the Lake District. Such axes have been found in the ditches of causewayed enclosures, so it is possible that Blewburton Hill was first altered by folk whose ancestral tomb was the Churn long barrow, four kilometres to the south.

A SETTLEMENT IN BLEWBURY VILLAGE

As Blewbury prepared for Christmas in 1983, the owners of a house on the London Road discovered a pair of pits on the spot where they were building a garage. These were excavated and were found to contain flint tools, pottery sherds, split pebbles, pieces of bone and antler, as well as cereal grains and hazelnut shells. From the presence of an arrowhead with a chisel-like tip, the finds have been dated to the Late Neolithic, a time that was to see the coming of great change for the people living around Aston Tirrold and Blewbury. The pits may simply have been used to dispose of household waste; however, many of the flint tools were in pristine condition, so this might have been a deliberate, ritual deposit of a kind found in both of the Neolithic and the following Bronze Age. Pits used for ritual deposits are often within or close to settlements and ritual enclosures, so it is possible that either or both could have existed in Blewbury in Neolithic times.

The Neolithic period in Britain lasted from about 6,000 to 4,500 years ago and was brought to an end by changes so profound that they could be said to have initiated the modern era we know today. Although wheat was planted and animals tended throughout the Neolithic period, families remained mobile, possibly planting wheat seed in the spring before moving with their stock to the higher pastures of the Downs or the Chilterns for the summer, and grateful if they returned in the autumn to find a decent crop to bolster their winter food supplies. The first major change was the move to a settled form of agriculture and the creation of field systems forming a quilted pattern of low banks or lynchets, such as those that were still clearly visible from the Ridgeway on Warren Down at Streatley in the middle of the 20th century. People became more tied to particular pieces of land, and so were more dependent on fewer food sources, but now they had greater control over them than over the wild animals and plants that had hitherto formed a substantial part of their diet.

BRONZE AGE BARROWS

At that time on the downs south of

© BERNARD MATTIMORE

This Mesolithic flint microlith is about 2.5 cm long from Gatehampton Farm. A number of these were set into a wooden shaft to create a viciously effective arrow or spear, kindly lent by Philip Turner.

Striking flakes from a specially prepared flint "core". A hammer-stone and an antler punch are being used to create the flakes that will be turned into microliths.

© RICHARD HOOK

Blewburton Hill, round barrow tombs were built. In the dry valleys they are often found in clusters, whereas on the crests of the hilltops single barrows are more common, sited a little below the summits, so that people looking up from the lower ground could have seen them clearly on the skyline. Not only had the shape of the tomb changed from rectangular to circular, but these new tombs usually held only one person, placed in the centre of the mound. In the Early Bronze Age the burials were usually of whole bodies, some with rich grave goods of gold and fine bronze weapons. Towards the middle of the Bronze Age around 3,500 years ago, there were more cremations with the ashes placed in distinctively decorated pots.

Whatever the form of the burial, this may for the first time indicate the appearance of a class of individual who held a position of clear and singular authority. Perhaps such a chief, whose people lived in and around Blewbury was buried in Churn Knob, the barrow that can still be seen silhouetted against the southern sky, a memorial and a marker of legitimacy for the chief's heirs. The mound is about twenty-five metres in diameter and, when built, was surrounded by the circular ditch from which it was quarried. The ditch is now filled in, but its location about five metres from the edge of the barrow is still detectable by the darker soil. Just ten metres southwest of Churn Knob stood a smaller barrow, which has been destroyed by ploughing, as have so many prehistoric sites since the coming of mechanised farming.

Mesolithic leather worker using bone needles and sinew for thread.

© Richard Hook

THE DISCOVERY OF METAL

The first use of metal can be added to agriculture and the rise in importance of the individual as a third major change affecting the people living around Blewburton some 4,000 years ago. For over two million years humans had used stone and wood to make tools and weapons. Yet the first use of bronze, an alloy of tin and copper, produced no immediate alteration in the way of life. It seems that it was not used simply to replace flint, but to create objects of high value, such as beautifully fashioned axe heads that reflected the status of their owners. Flint tools were still used for everyday scraping, cutting and piercing, but their makers no longer expended enough time to produce the finely made tools of the Neolithic, although they retained the skill to make perfect little "tanged and barbed" flint arrowheads for hunting and for warfare.

GREAT DITCHES

Three thousand years ago the people of the Bronze Age had stopped building round barrows on the Downs above Blewbury and Aston Tirrold. Exactly where they disposed of bodies is something of a mystery, although it is possible that rivers became the last resting places for most people. Human effort was probably largely expended in farming and, for some, the growing craft specialisations such as metalwork. There is one striking exception: Grims Ditches were constructed across the landscape in the Late Bronze Age, like the one that can be seen on Aston Upthorpe Downs. In fact this is one of the visible portions of a ditch-and-bank that runs across the Downs, from the Thames near Streatley to south of Lockinge, staying for the most part within a kilometre or so of the Ridgeway track. In a clear sign of continuity of tradition, the Grims Ditch skirts the Churn long barrow and a round barrow near Churn Farm. It may have been an agricultural or territorial boundary but nobody knows its real purpose, which is true of most prehistoric monuments not explicitly associated with burials. The name "Grims Ditch" was given to these features some 2,000 years later; "Grim" being an Anglo-Saxon nickname for the god Woden. It seems likely that "Grim" came to mean "the Devil" after the conversion to Christianity. Towards the end of the Bronze Age, the fortification of hilltops started. At Rams Hill, thirty kilometres to the west of Blewburton Hill, an existing settlement was first enclosed by a ditch-and-bank, a defence that was augmented at the end of the Bronze Age with a "box-rampart" made of timber and earth, a construction style that was also used at Blewburton Hill. Such defences not only reflected the wealth and prestige of the tribe but also signalled an increase in warfare between tribes. These defences were necessary to

© BERNARD MATTIMORE

A tranchet axe or adze, about 15 cm long from Gatehampton farm. This flint tool was skilfully worked to produce a strong, sharp blade edge. It was probably fitted with a wooden haft and used for working wood in the later Mesolithic around 7,000 years ago, kindly lent by Philip Turner.

© Bernard Mattimore

A fine late Bronze Age socketed axe 12.6 cms long and weighing 450 grams, found close to Blewburton Hill. It is of a pattern that was common in the south of England about 3,000 years ago. Kindly lent by Gary Horn.

counter the increased potency of marauding warrior groups, armed with a growing armoury of bronze weapons such as swords and spears.

Life around Blewburton Hill, from the beginning of the Mesolithic period to the start of the Iron Age in the 8th century BC, was punctuated by immense changes. The hunter-gatherer lifestyle gradually changed to one of settled agriculture; the landscape was no longer seen simply as a place to move through and hunt in, but rather as something that could be moulded to satisfy human needs. Yet the last two hundred years have produced changes just as profound, in which we can trace patterns of continuity of attitude, belief and social cohesion. Such continuity existed then as now, and persisted into the Iron Age, a period that came to mark the end of prehistory, and the beginning of our history.

STAN HUGHES

FURTHER READING
1. BARBER, M., C. DYER & A. OSWALD. 2001. THE CREATION OF MONUMENTS: NEOLITHIC CAUSEWAYED ENCLOSURES IN THE BRITISH ISLES. SWINDON
2. BARTON, N. 1993. STONE AGE BRITAIN. LONDON
3. BRADLEY, R. 1998. THE SIGNIFICANCE OF MONUMENTS. LONDON
4. BUTLER, C. 2005. PREHISTORIC FLINTWORK. STROUD
5. CUNLIFFE, B. 1994. THE OXFORD ILLUSTRATED HISTORY OF PREHISTORIC EUROPE. OXFORD
6. GIBSON, A. 2002. PREHISTORIC POTTERY OF BRITAIN & IRELAND. STROUD
7. HARDING, A.F. 2000. EUROPEAN SOCIETIES IN THE BRONZE AGE. CAMBRIDGE
8. HUNTER, J. & I.RALSTON.1999. THE ARCHAEOLOGY OF BRITAIN. LONDON
9. MALONE, C. 2001. NEOLITHIC BRITAIN AND IRELAND. STROUD
10. PARKER-PEARSON, M. 2005. BRONZE AGE BRITAIN. LONDON
11. PITTS, M. 2001. HENGEWORLD. LONDON
12. STRINGER, C. & P. ANDREWS. 2005. THE COMPLETE WORLD OF HUMAN EVOLUTION. LONDON

SHADOWS ON THE LANDSCAPE
RECENT ARCHAEOLOGICAL DISCOVERIES

Major construction projects in our region have given rise to recent archaeological research, funded by developers. The County Council Archaeology team advises local planning authorities on the implications of development proposals and recommends appropriate action. Much of this research is fully published, but some is currently available only as "grey literature": the unpublished reports and datasets that are the midway process between investigation and full publication. This three-part study is based on both published and as yet unpublished reports of the most interesting local archaeological investigations.

Shadows on the landscape 2006. Evidence of a late Neolithic settlement was found during the excavation of a Saxon cemetery before the construction of Didcot B Power Station.

PART I: NEOLITHIC TO BRONZE AGE

Around 2,800 years ago, at the end of the Bronze Age, an observer gazing northwards from Blewburton Hill would have seen a number of smoke plumes rising from the patchwork of woodland, grassland and arable beyond. Light, wispy columns from the hearths of homes, and darker webs that writhed between trunks and covered treetops as stumps were burnt to allow the plough to bite or the cattle to graze.

Except for its elevated location and its enclosure by a timber palisade, the settlement on top of Blewburton Hill may have looked similar to that of its neighbours in the landscape below. But while it may also have practised agriculture, it might have originated as a stock enclosure, or a storage and exchange centre for produce. It is strategically situated on the edge of the chalk downs overlooking the fertile greensand and clays of the Vale, the gravels and floodplains of the Thames Valley. It is also close to the main communication routes of the Thames and the Ridgeway. It may have participated in the growing success and stability of the land management surrounding it, and the increase in territoriality and power through systems of exchange.

This expanding agricultural landscape had been evolving for a considerable time. Over the previous 1,000 years, Bronze Age farms had multiplied, creating an ordered patchwork of clearings in the blanket of broadleaved woodland. Before that, there had been many millennia of human impact on the landscape, and its biomass. This narrative summarises those activities through the recent work of archaeological organisations investigating development projects.

THE NEOLITHIC (C 4,200 TO 2,200 BC)

By the fourth millennium BC, there are tantalising vestiges that hint at the use of this landscape by Neolithic pastoralists and cultivators. The communal monuments that survive as substantial landmarks suggest organisational power in a complex and formalised social structure. We still have little evidence for the settlements of those families and related groups that built Waylands Smithy, or the long barrow on Blewbury Down. Current evidence suggests that their settlements were further to the north in the flat plains of the Thames Valley, and on the edges of the greensand. The Downs may have been used for seasonal transhumance and as one focus of socio-religious activity.

The "Sites and Monuments Record" has information on the find-spots of numerous Neolithic artefacts, including polished stone axes from Didcot and many flint flakes and tools from the Downs. Development archaeology occasionally produces fragments of evidence of this crucial period. For example, during the excavation of a Saxon cemetery before construction of Didcot B Power Station, Oxford Archaeology found a late Neolithic (3,000 to 2,200 BC) ditch that probably formed part of a settlement or stock enclosure [5]. More recently, the archaeological evaluations carried out as part of the Didcot West (Great Western Park) proposal found scatters of late Mesolithic and early Neolithic flintwork (around 5,000 to 4,000 BC). A pit was also found that contained flint tempered pottery sherds and several soft hammer flint flakes, suggesting an early Neolithic date [16].

When a Transco gas pipeline was run from Ipsden in South

Oxfordshire to Scotland in West Berkshire, Oxford Archaeology made an important find, just across the Thames at South Stoke [1 & 22]. Seven rubbish pits of Middle Neolithic date contained the probable remains of debris from domestic hearths. This included 485 flint flakes and tools, 340 sherds of pottery from ten individual cups and bowls, charred wheat grains, oats, charred hazel nuts and small fragments of cattle and pig bones. There were also quantities of charcoal, mainly from shrubs such as hawthorn, blackthorn, and hazel, that were presumably the remains of firewood. Some wood from larger forest trees such as oak, ash and alder was also present. These pits and their contents are very similar to the later Neolithic pits found in Blewbury.

The pottery resembles the plain and decorated bowls of the mid-4th millennium BC (about 3700 to 3350 BC) and this is confirmed by several radiocarbon dates from the charred hazel nuts. The mix of shrubby and broad-leaved timber and the bones of cattle and pigs may also indicate the range of landscapes in the immediate vicinity at the time. The shrubs tend to colonise downland or clearings, that would be grazed by cattle; the larger trees form dense woodland that is the natural habitat of the pig.

A tantalising piece of evidence came to light during another, more recent Transco Pipeline project [18]. Only 500 metres from Blewburton Hill, and just north of the Aston Upthorpe Road, at Site 29, the archaeologists found two small pits and a ditch. Although they did not obtain clear dating evidence from these features, stratigraphic evidence led them to suggest an early/middle Neolithic date. If there was, as has been suggested, a Neolithic causewayed enclosure on Blewburton Hill, could this tenuous evidence be related to it?

THE BRONZE AGE (2,200 TO 750 BC)

Several Middle Bronze Age farmsteads were discovered in the Clay Vale area west of Abingdon in the 1990s [13, 3, 11, 12, 15, 23, 24 & 25]. These farms were relatively small, often based in woodland clearings. They usually comprised a series of rectilinear "home closes" within which were the dwellings and ancillary buildings of the farm, and these gave access to the unenclosed land beyond. These sites confirm that, by the Middle Bronze Age, land close to the river valleys was

In 1991, during the Tesco development at Didcot, a very rare find of a Middle Bronze Age farm was excavated. At 3,800 years old this is the oldest farm to be discovered in our locality. Its rectilinear fields may have been for stock; poorly preserved faunal evidence hints at the raising of sheep and goats, but the presence of deer bones shows that hunting was still important. Other artefacts suggest that, at least 4,000 years ago the population living at Tesco's was already establishing open settlements.

undergoing a systematic, radical process of division and management. The evidence also suggests that these farms specialised in animal husbandry, and that cereal production was not the main activity.

By the late Bronze Age, certainly by the 8th century BC, there were hilltop settlements enclosed by palisade-fences, including that on Blewburton Hill. It is probably no coincidence that the great linear ditch systems also appear around this time. Clear local patterns of 8th century BC pottery have been identified, with distinctive decorative traits in north Wiltshire, Berkshire and south Oxfordshire, This local patterning has "a sharp cut-off along the edge of the chalk overlooking the Thames Valley and conform[s] to the line of the Berkshire Grims Ditch" [4]. Present evidence suggests that the location of enclosed sites, like the one on Blewburton Hill, was due to their social and economic function, rather than simply defence. This was based on the acquisition, strategic control and consumption of produce and elite goods. Social and economic power appears to have been acquired through trade.

It is probable that the settlement on Blewburton Hill was established at the interface of social, geographic and economic areas, between the chalk upland and the Thames Valley. This may have been as a response to territorial tensions, or perhaps it was designed to act as a centre both for storage and exchange. Its strategic location could have made it an ideal late Bronze Age "trading post".

PAUL SMITH
OXFORDSHIRE COUNTY ARCHAEOLOGIST.

REFERENCES ARE TO BE FOUND AFTER "SHADOWS ON THE LANDSCAPE PART III".

(Right): Reconstruction of the Iron Age gateway and ramparts on Blewburton Hill. Although clearly defensible there is no evidence of siege or warfare on the hill fort. It was probably used primarily as a centre of agricultural and economic activity.

TIMES OF CHANGE
THE IRON AGE AND ROMAN PERIODS

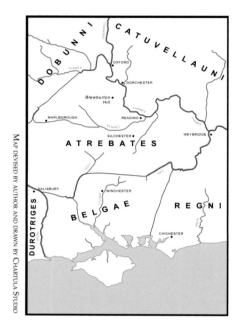

MAP DEVISED BY AUTHOR AND DRAWN BY CHARTULA STUDIO

Possible tribal, territorial boundaries in the late Iron Age.

THE UPPER THAMES VALLEY IN THE IRON AGE

The theory that the beginning of the Iron Age was marked by invasion of newcomers bringing new technology is no longer widely credited. Archaeology in the last fifty years now suggests much greater continuity from the Bronze Age to the Iron Age, with major changes occurring gradually over an extended period. The climate was deteriorating at the start of the early Iron Age in the 8th century BC, eventually becoming wetter and colder by as much as two degrees Celsius, thereby shortening the growing season; nevertheless, the population seems to have increased. This required the intensification of agriculture. More land was made available by clearing forests on high ground, and the "Celtic" fields were established on the Downs. The field system at Unhill Bottom, south of Aston Tirrold may date to the Iron Age.

There was an increasing trend towards autumn and winter sown arable land. During the 1st millennium BC, a more diverse range of crops was introduced, dominated by spelt, six-row barley, breadwheat and beans; these displaced emmer wheat and naked barley. The gathering of wild plants declined, as did fishing and hunting wild fowl and animals (though bones of deer, pine martin and badger have been found). By this time, bones of domestic animals, notably sheep, cattle and pigs, are common. From the predominance of elderly female sheep bones, and finds of loom weights, it seems that sheep were kept mainly for wool and milk rather than meat. Horses were kept but, as now, were high status animals and not a food source. Bees had been introduced by the middle Iron Age (400 to 100BC).

Most people lived in rural farmsteads, typically in circular houses scattered across the overwhelmingly agricultural landscape. Grain was stored either in square granaries raised above ground to discourage vermin or, on well-drained land, in storage pits dug into the ground. Caesar wrote: "The population is numerous, their homesteads clustered together and very like those in Gaul, and there are many cattle. For money they use either bronze or gold coins or iron bars of fixed standard

Iron Age traders.

weight." And Strabo said: "...
they are ruled by chieftains. The
forests are their towns...and they make huts there for themselves and
their cattle."

These sites were normally undefended except perhaps by ditches
to protect livestock from wild animals. However, in addition to these
undefended settlements, hillforts were occupied (possibly from the
Bronze Age) and defensive earthworks built – Blewburton Hill is not
untypical.

*Skeleton of a dog buried on
Blewburton Hill in the Iron
Age, fifty centimetres high at the
shoulder.*

BLEWBURTON IN THE IRON AGE
Four archaeological excavations
were undertaken on Blewburton
Hill between 1947 and 1967, the
first three led by A E P Collins and
the last, with a re-interpretation of
the earlier work, by D W Harding.
Although the digs were limited
in extent, pottery finds showed
settlement there during much of
the Iron Age and indeed some
pottery even indicated possible late

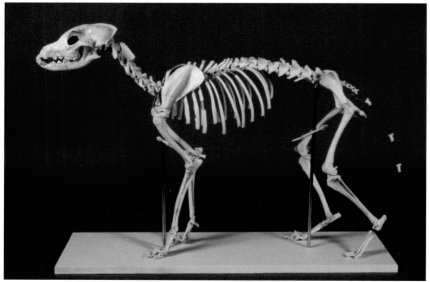

© RICHARD HOOK

© READING MUSEUM SERVICE (READING BOROUGH COUNCIL)

Iron Age Ox Cart.

© Richard Hook

Bronze Age occupation.

Today the most prominent earthworks on Blewburton Hill are the parallel terraces around the western end. These are the strip-lynchets (agricultural terraces), which are thought to be of medieval origin but could possibly be much earlier. Above these sit the defensive earthworks of the Iron Age – now much ploughed out with the stratification damaged by rabbits! At least three distinct phases of defensive works were undertaken, using different techniques. The first was a simple palisade, which probably enclosed only the western half of the hilltop. The second phase, probably dating from the 6th or 5th century, was a much more sophisticated box rampart surrounded by a deep V-shaped ditch now enclosing the whole eleven acres of the hill top. The final phase of fortification came much later, probably late 2nd or early 1st century, and was built as a dump rampart.

The defences had a gateway at the western end of the enclosure, and this has been thoroughly excavated. It had a pair of gates, possibly with a footway overhead and a double carriageway, surfaced with quartzite and chalk cobbles, running between them. From the excavations there was not much evidence of buildings, as the digs were concentrated more on the Iron Age defences and the later Saxon burials. Within the interior, limited excavations revealed numerous post holes, but no clear linear or circular patterns were seen. We can only speculate therefore that there were probably many roundhouses on the site, perhaps similar to the reconstructions built in recent years at Butser Hill. The large house built there was closely based on an excavation at Pimperne in Dorset. This needed thirty-six, fifty-year-old trees for the main supporting posts, fifty-seven young trees for the outer wall posts,

fifty-five trees for rafters and seven tonnes
of thatching straw. Nevertheless just two
men, with no sophisticated tools or lifting
gear, built the house between them. A
search for buildings on Blewburton Hill
would clearly be a fascinating undertaking for
future archaeology.

Iron Age Pottery Maker.

© Richard Hook

Long-term settlement of the site in the
Iron Age is not in doubt although it may
not have been continuous. There
have been many finds of artefacts
indicating sustained habitation,
as well as numerous pits of a type
used for storing grain. Much of the evidence
for the chronology of the site comes from changes in pottery styles: at
Blewburton, as at most prehistoric sites, potsherds are the most common
finds. Other finds include a number of quern stones, pounding stones,
chalk and baked clay spindle whorls, and bone and antler tools. A
bronze ring and some small iron implements have been found, as well as
a sword shaped iron currency bar.

Perhaps some of the most interesting finds are the skeletons of
animals. Collins reported "Lying on the street and under the fallen
masses of stones...were several corpses. Thus, skulls of a horse and
a cow were lying in the centre of the street" and "under the south
revetment wall lay the skeleton of a deer, complete and articulated
except for its hind quarters. Under the fallen northern wall...lay two
complete horse skeletons." Harding argues, "the distribution of the
horse-skeletons in the entrance in pairs, and in particular the situation
of another buried in its own pit...[indicates] quite clearly, we are here
dealing with a deliberate ritual of horse-burial." The most dramatic of
these burials contained the skeletons of a horse and a man. The man's
head had been dislocated from his body and placed within the rib cage
of the horse. An iron adze, sherds of a large burnished black pot, over
a hundred quartzite pebbles and a dog skeleton were also associated
with the burial. Similar ritual deposits of animal, and indeed human,
skeletons in pits have been found at other Iron Age sites. There is no

Claudius
Special coin struck to commemorate the Claudian conquest of Britain in 43 AD. This example, found near Blewbury, is made of iron covered in silver. Part of the silver has eroded away. The reverse shows a triumphal arch surmounted by an equestrian statue and with DE BRITANN on the architrave. Lent by Gary Horn.

evidence of settlement on the Iron Age hillfort at Blewburton beyond the end of the 1st century BC.

TRIBAL SOCIETY AND POLITICS IN THE LATE IRON AGE

Around 100BC, as Rome turned its attention to Gaul, Belgic tribes crossed the channel into southeast Britain. The final phase of the Blewburton defences seems to belong to the period shortly before the arrival of the Belgic tribes, and was perhaps a defence against them. There is, however, no evidence of any major battle, or sack, on the site. In any event, many hillforts, including Blewburton, were finally abandoned around this time in favour of settlements on low ground, a cultural change in Belgic and non-Belgic areas alike.

Caesar's short-lived invasions of Britain in 55 and 54BC had little direct impact on Oxfordshire, but there is clear evidence of increasing contact with the Roman Empire, particularly through trade and cultural exchange with Romanised Gaul. Amphorae and luxury vessels from Italy have been found in late Iron Age graves elsewhere in Britain. Although the economy was still dominated by agriculture, there was a growth in craftwork, notably in the production of rich metalwork such as the "great torc" (gold neck ring) of about 70BC found at Snettisham. Such rich objects indicate a stratified society with sufficient surplus to support an elite class. However, no such treasures have yet been found on Blewburton Hill!

Roman influence was also seen in the establishment of oppida (proto-towns) around the turn of the millennium. The nearest to Blewburton is Silchester (southwest of Reading), set on a modest ridge offering some natural defence, which was strengthened in the late Iron Age by earthworks. There is little evidence of occupation until the last quarter of the 1st century BC. A planned street grid with metalled streets show Roman influence; there were round and rectangular buildings. This may have been the capital of the Atrebates' kingdom. The low lying late Iron Age site of Dyke Hills, across the Thames from Wittenham Clumps, was fore-runner of the small Roman town of Dorchester; it may have served as a contact point between disparate social groups. Although tribal boundaries were fluid and are not now precisely known, Blewburton might have been a strategic stronghold close to the key boundaries between the Atrebates (a Belgic tribe) to the southeast, the Dubunni (a native British tribe) to the west and the Catuvellauni (British) attacking from the northeast. In 40AD Verica, king of the Atrebates, fled to Rome as the Catuvellauni overran his land, perhaps precipitating the Roman invasion three years later. The northern territory of the Atrebates, perhaps including Blewburton Hill, had already been taken by the Catuvellauni around a decade earlier.

THE ROMAN PERIOD

The old tribal politics of the Iron Age still played a role, even after Claudius' invasion of 43AD. The Catuvellauni were defeated by Roman troops and the Atrebates' kingdom seems to have been restored. By 51AD Cogidubnus was king; his territory covered the Regini (in Chichester) the Belgae (Winchester) and the Atrebates (Silchester), and was ruled as a client kingdom of Rome, not part of the Province of Britannia. Dorchester on Thames was also a regional capital and again boundaries are uncertain – we do not know which city controlled the area around Blewburton.

Blewburton Hill was not itself occupied in Roman times but there is much evidence of settlement in the surrounding region. Finds of Roman pottery on the hill represent chance deposits (eg. picnics!) rather than occupation. Other nearby Roman sites include a number of villas.

Of particular interest is the Roman Temple on top of Lowbury Hill near the Ridgeway, at 186 metres one of the highest points on the Downs south of Blewbury. Though there is evidence of late Bronze Age and late Iron Age use of the site, there was clearly far more activity there between mid 3rd and late 4th centuries AD (see box).

About a kilometre from Lowbury Hill, on Roden Downs, lies another Roman site. Here there was a large enclosure, about 250 metres square. Inside its southeast edge was a cremating place from the early Roman period (1st to early 2nd century AD). Beside this was a burial ground with ten graves from the late Roman period (4th to 5th century). There were traces of wooden coffins, and one with a lead lining. Nothing is now visible, due to heavy ploughing.

Evidence for Roman settlement in the low-lying areas around Blewburton is plentiful, for example near Aston Tirrold, Brightwell-cum-

© BERNARD MATTIMORE

Nero
Also found near Blewbury this silver coin depicts Nero, successor to Claudius and Emperor from 54 to 68 AD. Lent by Gary Horn.

BIBLIOGRAPHY
1. BOON, G. (1974) SILCHESTER: THE ROMAN TOWN OF CALLEVA (REVISED ED), NEWTON ABBOT, DAVID & CHARLES; 2. BRIGGS, G. COOK, J. AND ROWLEY, T. (1986) THE ARCHAEOLOGY OF THE OXFORD REGION, OXFORD, OUDES; 3. COLLINS, A.E.P. (1947) EXCAVATIONS ON BLEWBURTON HILL, 1947 BERKSHIRE ARCHAEOLOGICAL JOURNAL 50; 4. COLLINS, A.E.P. (1953) EXCAVATIONS ON BLEWBURTON HILL, 1948 AND 1949 BERKSHIRE ARCHAEOLOGICAL JOURNAL 53; 5. COLLINS, A.E.P. AND COLLINS , F.J. (1959) EXCAVATIONS ON BLEWBURTON HILL,1953 BERKSHIRE ARCHAEOLOGICAL JOURNAL 5; 6. CUNLIFFE, B (1993) WESSEX TO AD1000, HARLOW, LONGMAN; 7. DAVIES, J.A. (1985) THE ROMAN COINS FROM LOWBURY HILL, OXFORD, OXONIENSA; 8. FULFORD, M. AND RIPPON, S.J. (1994) LOWBURYHILL: A RE-ASSESSMENT OF THE PROBABLE ROMANO-CELTIC TEMPLE AND THE ANGLO-SAXON BARROW, ARCHAEOLOGICAL JOURNAL 151; 9. FULFORD, M. AND TIMBY, J. (2000) LATE IRON AGE AND ROMAN SILCHESTER, LONDON, SOCIETY FOR THE PROMOTION OF ROMAN STUDIES; 10. FULFORD, M. (2002) A GUIDE TO SILCHESTER: THE ROMAN TOWN OF CALLEVA ATREBATUM, READING, MUSEUM OF READING; 11. GOODMAN, M. (1997) THE ROMAN WORLD, LONDON, ROUTLEDGE; 12. HARDING, D.W. (1976) BLEWBURTON HILL, BERKSHIRE: RE-EXCAVATION AND REAPPRAISAL IN HILLFORTS; LATER PREHISTORIC EARTHWORKS IN BRITAIN AND IRELAND, LONDON; 13. HAYES, A (1993) ARCHAEOLOGY OF THE BRITISH ISLES, LONDON, BATSFORD; 14. HENIG, M.AND BOOTH, P. (2000) ROMAN OXFORDSHIRE, SUTTON; 15. HOOD, S. AND WALTON, H. (1948) EXCAVATIONS ON RODEN DOWN, TRANSACTIONS OF NEWBURY AND DISTRICT FIELD CLUB VOL IX; 16. LEWIS, N. AND REINHOLD, M. EDS. (1990) ROMAN CIVILIZATION: SELECTED READINGS. VOLUME II: THE EMPIRE, 3RD EDITION, NEW YORK, CUP.; 17. MASSEY, R. (1999) BLEWBURTON HILL: AN ARCHAEOLOGICAL EVALUATION, ENGLISH HERITAGE; 18. SALWAY, P. (1984) ROMAN BRITAIN: A VERY SHORT INTRODUCTION, OXFORD, OUP; 19. SELLWOOD, L. (1985) TRIBAL BOUNDARIES VIEWED FROM THE PERSPECTIVE OF NUMISMATIC EVIDENCE, IN ASPECTS OF THE IRON AGE IN CENTRAL SOUTHERN BRITAIN; 20. WACHER, J. (1974) THE TOWNS OF ROMAN BRITAIN, LONDON, BATSFORD; 21. WELLS, C. (1984) THE ROMAN EMPIRE, LONDON, FONTANA

Sotwell, Coscote and Upton. However, no excavations have taken place at these sites and so little is presently known.

INTO THE DARK AGES

Roman Britain had started to decline by the mid 3rd century. The civitas capitals began to lose their administrative function and masonry defences were necessary around many towns. While these problems arose on a local scale, the province and the empire as a whole were undergoing a series of calamities. The emperor Magnentius usurped power in 350AD, Britain (as far south as the Thames) was invaded by barbarians in 367-370 and the legions withdrew in 388, 401 and 409. Finally, in 410AD, the emperor Honorius declined the cities' requests for assistance and told them to look to their own defence. It was over. However, the cities were not immediately deserted. At Silchester, Fulford says, there is "no evidence of abandonment before the 5th century" but it "cannot be regarded as a town in a Roman sense much after the middle decades of the 5th century." In the Roman period, coins had been introduced to the province primarily to pay the army, and from there found their way into general circulation. With the army gone, and with no stable central authority, no new coin was introduced and "by about 430AD coin-using in a market system was at an end."

Germanic materials have been found at various locations in southern Britain dating from the late 4th century; it seems likely that small scale settlement was permitted by the Romano-British, at least from early in the 5th century, possibly to help with defence of the cities.

The alignment of all the major roads out of Silchester has been preserved for considerable distances, except for that leading to Dorchester. A defensive dyke was built across this road, suggesting that there was a political frontier here, between competing Germanic tribes or possibly between the remaining British at Silchester and Saxons at Dorchester. It seems that, after the Roman interlude, the area around Blewburton Hill may once again have been at the centre of tribal politics.

DR DAVE CARLESS

ACKNOWLEDGEMENT FOR LOWBURY HILL BOX (OPPOSITE)
THE ASSISTANCE OF CHERRY GRAY OF THE OXFORDSHIRE COUNTY MUSEUM SERVICE AT WOODSTOCK IS GRATEFULLY ACKNOWLEDGED IN ALLOWING PHOTOGRAPHS TO BE TAKEN. WOODSTOCK MUSEUM HAS A FASCINATING AND EXTENSIVE DISPLAY OF ROMAN FINDS FROM LOWBURY HILL AND ELSEWHERE.

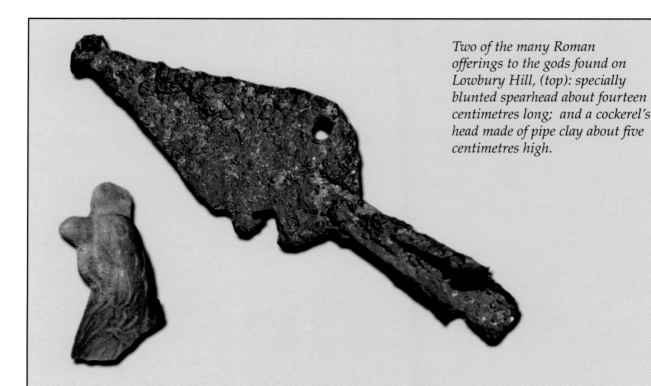

PHOTOGRAPHS TAKEN BY KIND PERMISSION OF OXFORDSHIRE COUNTY MUSEUM SERVICE

Two of the many Roman offerings to the gods found on Lowbury Hill, (top): specially blunted spearhead about fourteen centimetres long; and a cockerel's head made of pipe clay about five centimetres high.

LOWBURY HILL TEMPLE

The rectangular enclosure on top of Lowbury Hill has attracted attention ever since the mid 19th century, when it was thought to have been a Roman fort. Today only a surrounding earth bank remains, but in 1844 "some slight vestiges of a praetorium or general's abode" were reported as "discernible" in the centre. Visitors collected coins and oyster shells there, and antiquarians sampled the site. In 1914, archaeologists excavated the whole enclosure. Many roof tiles, and a small patch of rough paving a little south of the centre, were the only traces of a building. Whatever had stood there had been as thoroughly cleared away as the rectangular flint wall which once enclosed the site. The archaeologists concluded that this had been a farmstead.

Towards the end of the 20th century, Reading archaeologists examined the site again. They were able to show that the wall was probably built in the mid second century, replacing an earlier wooden enclosure. The bank consisted of earth from the foundation trench. A skeleton, buried in that trench, was placed there after the wall was demolished, sometime around 600 AD.

More than a thousand Roman coins have been found, largely dating to the late Roman period. Other votive deposits include iron weapons, some of which seem to have been deliberately degraded, similar to weapons found at other ritual sites. Jewellery deposits included brooches, pins, finger rings and bracelets. The weapons could indicate an association with the god Mars. Two other possible cult objects from there were a child's rattle, which may be associated with Isis, and the head of a white clay statuette of a cock, which may be associated with Mercury. The ram is also linked to Mercury, and a large collection of sheep bones was found on Lowbury Hill.

In the 7th century, the place still had enough prestige to attract a rich Saxon burial, set in a substantial barrow just fifteen metres east of the enclosure, and opposite the entrance to the Roman site. The name of the hill still reflects both structures: Low from the Saxon hlaw for "barrow" and Bury from the Saxon burh for "enclosure".

SHADOWS ON THE LANDSCAPE
RECENT ARCHAEOLOGICAL DISCOVERIES

© BERNARD MATTIMORE

Major construction projects in our region have given rise to recent archaeological research, funded by developers.

PART II:

THE IRON AGE (750 TO AD43)

By about 750 BC, iron working was slowly emerging, but bronze continued for a considerable time to be the basic metal for tools and weapons, and all metals would have been regularly recycled. There is even evidence suggesting that flint still continued in use as a cheap and simple addition to the tool kit [e.g. 17]. As iron grew more common, clearance of woodland became increasingly rapid and farms expanded, taking in extensive new areas of land.

Cotswold Archaeology has found evidence for this expansion [RPS 2003] to the west of Didcot. An extensive settlement that probably began around the end of the Bronze Age and the beginning of the Iron Age, and peaked about 2,200 to 2,400 years ago, was discovered on the high ground. Field ditches, postholes of structures, and numerous grain storage pits were recorded. The main occupation area was enclosed on its western and northern sides (along the break of slope) by a substantial ditch. This settlement was positioned to have a superb view across the Thames Valley to the north, where many more farmsteads and field systems would have been visible, and where the lush spring grazing would have been a valuable energy source for cattle. The same view is now dominated by a rather different energy source - the monolithic, huddled grey cooling towers of Didcot Power Station.

The main evidence for this period comes from the Abingdon Reservoir proposal [13], and various unpublished evaluation reports ibid]. Investigations using many techniques including field walking, geophysical survey, aerial photography and trial trenching have, for the first time, allowed us to look at a fourteen-square-kilometre area of landscape in the

Clay Vale south of the River Ock.

In the 1930s the Vale was considered to be an area of impenetrable primeval forest and marsh, devoid of prehistoric occupation. By the 1970s some scholars were questioning this view, but even so, in the 1980s it was still commonly suggested that, in the Iron Age and Roman periods "The Vale may have formed an unpopulated divide between a densely occupied north Wessex Zone and an equally densely populated Upper Thames Zone" [14].

We now know that at least eleven settlements existed in this area south of the Ock by about 500 to 300 BC, but there is currently little evidence to show that many of these farms survived into the later years of the Iron Age. This could be indicative of political and social flux at this time that may have influenced local economy and land-use. Or it may be related to changing drainage problems of the Thames and its tributaries, but reoccupation in the Roman period would not seem to support this.

A similar settlement was found when, in 2002, John Moore Heritage Services carried out an excavation in advance of the construction of the Rutherford Appleton Diamond Synchrotron Project at Harwell. [9,10 & 17]. While the site produced some Mesolithic flintwork and Bronze Age pottery, the first confirmed occupation appears to be an enclosed early to middle Iron Age farmstead with numerous grain storage pits that contained the carbonised grains of wheat and hulled barley. The excavators suggested that the farm's economy was probably based on agriculture rather than livestock. By the late Iron Age the farmstead appears to have shifted about 200 metres to the west. This later settlement continued into the Roman period (see below). The vast metallic doughnut-shaped building that acts as a 'super microscope' and can now be seen from the A4185 represents the largest UK-funded scientific facility to be built for over thirty years. It sits where an Iron Age family grew their crops and raised their children. This piece of Oxfordshire landscape reflects the evolution of human endeavour, from hunter-gatherer and early subsistence farming to the age of quantum mechanics.

In 2003 more Iron Age sites came to light when extensive archaeological work was carried out by Network Archaeology, in advance of the 25 km long Transco natural gas pipeline from Chalgrove to East Ilsley [18]. One of these, (Site 22) was found west of Brightwell-cum-Sotwell.

The vast metallic doughnut-shaped Rutherford Appleton Laboratory's "Diamond" Synchrotron represents the largest UK-funded scientific facility to be built for over thirty years. It sits where an Iron Age family once grew their crops and raised their children.

This piece of Oxfordshire landscape reflects the evolution of human endeavour, from hunter-gatherer and early subsistence farming to the age of quantum mechanics.

This site extended for almost 500 metres along the 36-metre wide pipeline easement.

The smoke rising from the homes and new woodland clearings of this farmstead would have been visible to our observer on Blewburton Hill at the end of the Bronze and beginning of the Iron Age, for this appears to be the period when this settlement was first established. The archaeologists found sparse, but regular features along the whole length of this site proving that an agrarian field system was present and probably being expanded at this time. Two sinkholes were also found, one of which contained the poorly preserved remains of a later, Iron Age, human burial in the upper fills. For some reason, by around 500BC, there appears to have been a lull in settlement activity on this site.

At Blewburton Hill too, the evidence indicates a similar break in occupation around this time. However, at Blewburton Hill, this lull was followed by increased activity, with the construction of the first major defences – the massive and technologically advanced, possibly, six metre high box ramparts surrounded by a deep ditch. These echo the Hallstatt culture on the continent, and occur in England at hillforts such as Maiden Castle and Hod Hill in Dorset, and at Hollingbury in East Sussex. The Blewburton Hill defences were probably constructed sometime between 500 and 300 BC.

The Brightwell settlement also flourished again sometime in the 3rd century BC. A complex system of field boundary and enclosure ditches was investigated, as were several roundhouses, and it is clear that this settlement continued to expand and flourish. It not only survived into the Roman period, but by continued expansion and complexity of features, clearly thrived, although by this time the settlement appears to have shifted and this area has become its rural hinterland. Long-lived settlements such as this indicate that the late Iron Age pressures were not all negative, but that some sort of land-use rationalisation was taking place.

This pipeline also produced limited, but proven evidence for other settlements including Bronze Age pits near North Moreton, and a probable farmstead of later Bronze Age to early Iron Age date near South Moreton. The latter would have been contemporary with the first palisaded enclosure on Blewburton Hill.

The evidence from this major linear development is currently being analysed by many specialists. The results will provide an invaluable contribution to our understanding of the Iron Age and Romano-British settlement activity in the shadow of defended sites such as Blewburton Hill and Wittenham Clumps. Our knowledge of the Iron Age environs of the latter is being greatly extended by the work of Oxford Archaeology there.

During the later period of the Iron Age we see not only the expansion of farming, but also significant changes in other socio-economic processes. Some of these changes may have been influenced by the increasing stability and predictability of the agricultural regime that in turn led to population increases. By the 1st century BC, increasing territorial pressure, power struggles, and a growing culture, certainly within the elite of society, of overt material wealth, resulted in inevitable tensions between tribal groups. The area that is at the core of this project was one geographic hub of a probable struggle for dominance between the Catuvellauni to the north and east and the Attrebates to the south.

In the 1st century BC, after a period of apparent hiatus and neglect, newly constructed, massive dumped ramparts and deep ditches were dug to form the final phase of the defences on Blewburton Hill, providing a clear landmark. They also provide an indicator of the prevailing political and social stresses. However, current evidence from the unenclosed settlement sites already mentioned might suggest that many ordinary farming families were not seriously affected by these events during the final two centuries of the Iron Age. Perhaps the continuing success of these settled farming communities was, at least in part, to lead to the obsolescence of hillforts like Blewburton Hill.

On a moonlit night it is easy to see, in the mind's eye, the hearths and shadows of Iron Age people on Blewburton Hill.

During the 1st Century BC, as the inhabitants of Blewburton Hill scanned the surrounding countryside from behind their recently redeveloped and strengthened defences, they would probably have had mixed feelings, depending on which tribal group they held allegiance to. We cannot be certain if they watched the smoke from the hearths and smithies of

© Bernard Mattimore

their strongly defended neighbour on the not so distant range of low hills to the north with a feeling of security, or fear. But, the evidence indicates that by around 50 BC, the Catuvellauni had expanded their territory southwards. This probably included Blewburton Hill and its environs, and it may be significant that on present evidence, Blewburton Hill does not appear to have continued in use much beyond 50 BC. One thing is certain; these people would have been aware that they were living during a crucial time of change. And for those who held power, looming ever larger in their thoughts were the ambitions of the expanding empire just across the narrow sea channel.

Perhaps it was concerns such as these that encouraged the people occupying Blewburton Hill to bury the bodies of cattle, deer and horses inside the entranceway and the enclosure ditch. For we are beginning to understand through archaeological research, that such 'special deposits' were an important part of the belief systems of Iron Age people. Physical boundaries and animals held important symbolic meaning beyond their immediate worth as demarcation lines or valued possessions. The ancient myth of man and horse combined into one creature may have evolved from the idea that the horse represented a mediator between the "wild" of nature and the "domestic" under the control of humans. There is increasing evidence that the bodies of domestic animals were often deposited within occupied areas, near entrances, or in enclosure ditches around settlements – perhaps to signify (and appease?) the tensions between the controlled environment of the home, and the more unpredictable world beyond.

The horse was always a powerful symbol, and a high status animal. In our area, it appears in the late Bronze Age at Uffington as a significant landmark that could have visually "branded" the territory of a specific tribal group, just as the contemporary earthwork of Grims Ditch physically bounds the scarp of the Downs. It is remarkable that, not only has the chalk horse survived for the best part of three millennia, but also vital elements of the present economy and culture of this area of Oxfordshire still revolve around equestrian activities.

PAUL SMITH
OXFORDSHIRE COUNTY ARCHAEOLOGIST

ACKNOWLEDGEMENT
THE help of THE COUNCIL of the CENTRAL LABORATORY of the RESEARCH COUNCILS IS gratefully acknowledged for supplying recent aerial photographs of THE RUTHERFORD APPLETON LABORATORY "DIAMOND LIGHT SOURCE" AND surroundings.
REFERENCES ARE TO BE FOUND AFTER "SHADOWS ON THE LANDSCAPE PART III".

OUR ANGLO-SAXON ORIGINS
FROM THE EARLY FIFTH CENTURY TO THE NORMAN CONQUEST

© RICHARD HOOK

The Blewbury countryside in 1066 AD would be familiar to us: fundamental social and economic changes over the previous six hundred years had forged a landscape of coherent villages, clustered around their churches and set amidst open fields. But the area around Blewbury was, in the earlier Anglo-Saxon period, far from a sleepy country corner. This was an important border region, crucial to the emergence of the kingdom of Wessex, fought over by kings and made famous by Alfred the Great. The Thames - transport artery and corridor

Artist's impression of the village of Estone (now Aston Upthorpe) in the late Saxon period from the east side of Blewburton Hill.

to the Continent - was an important strategic and political prize, surrounded by valuable agricultural land. Throughout the period, farming people worked this land, more concerned with the round of agricultural activity than the haggling of the powerful. Yet here, around Blewbury, battles and political upheavals must at times have sorely disrupted their routines.

In the mid fifth century we would have felt less at home: smaller fields; areas of non-arable land more significant; farms and hamlets scattered. There were no villages, no churches. Frequent pagan burial grounds, like the one on the top of Blewburton Hill, provided a focus for these dispersed communities; the neglected or robbed-out remains of small Romano-British villas and farm buildings, such as those west of Didcot, were witness to cultural change.

These were not so much Dark Ages as different ages, a time when the withering of over-arching Roman authority, as described in a previous chapter, presented ambitious locals with an opportunity to create new, smaller-scale power structures. The demise of the previous Roman coin economy, trade, taxation and judicial system, once co-ordinated through now neglected towns like Silchester, inevitably meant that post-Roman arrangements were localised and varied. New bosses looked for new ways of proclaiming their status with buildings and possessions. In this fluid and complex environment, settlers - ordinary farming people as well as leaders - with new ideas and objects could have a considerable impact.

THE EARLY SAXONS

Near Blewbury this impact is obvious from very early in the post-Roman period. The Upper Thames valley around Abingdon and Dorchester is well known for a concentration of fifth century Germanic-style cemeteries and settlement. The new designs and buildings most closely matched those of northern Germany and the Low Countries. There are several cemeteries where, in a different and strikingly consistent ritual, men, women and children were buried with objects of changed design or manufacture. Usually only the metal things, like jewellery and weapons, or metal components such as belt buckles, as well as pottery survive. These objects help to date the burials, but also tell us that the family groups farming the Blewbury area had absorbed in their costume, pottery, weapons and ways of burying people, elements of Saxon culture.

The burial ground on Blewburton Hill, dug into the decaying though still prominent hill-fort in the fifth and sixth centuries, provided examples of these early brooches echoing Saxon styles, but also included objects linking the dead to the recent Roman past. There are other cemeteries, at Long Wittenham, Abingdon, Berinsfield and Didcot, with burials confirming that, across this area by the sixth century, local society was already re-grouping around a different cultural and political focus. Historians and archaeologists will continue to argue, but these changes in jewellery, weapons and burial practices can be explained as the surviving signs of the influence of immigration, combined with the adoption of new ways by local people with long roots in the area. The inclusion of possessions evoking the Roman past was just one way in which echoes of the previous period permeated the Anglo-Saxon age. Dorchester seems to have been an early power centre; perhaps local leaders based there assumed control over the surrounding region relatively quickly and efficiently and, whether with direct Saxon intervention or not, adopted Anglo-Saxon culture in consolidating their grasp on authority.

Blewbury's immediate environs, however, show a frustrating lack of Anglo-Saxon archaeology, having produced only a weapon or two and the odd bone comb. Perhaps much of the evidence is buried beneath the present villages. However, the two most significant archaeological sites, the early cemetery on Blewburton Hill and the later (seventh century) burial mound next to the Roman temple on Lowbury Hill, illustrate a fascinating aspect of early Anglo-Saxon society. Prehistoric and Romano-British sites, particularly those on high points or boundaries, like the temple and the hill-fort, were often re-used for burials: these special places in the landscape were attractive and powerful because they forged links with ancestral people and their past glories. The burial mound on Lowbury Hill covered a person of some distinction. At a time when kingdoms were beginning to cohere and gather strength, this important man was buried with an impressive display of weaponry and metal work including a sword, spearhead, shield, decorated bronze bowl and bone comb. The barrow must have been very prominent on the skyline and boasted wide views of the uplands of a landscape the occupant had presumably dominated.

We have scanty direct evidence for the earliest pattern of Anglo-Saxon farms and hamlets overlooked by Lowbury. However, drawing on nearby sites like Sutton Courtenay, and even Yarnton (where a huge modern excavation uncovered the story of a settlement for the whole Anglo-Saxon period), we know that before the eighth century the timber-built farms usually comprised small partly-sunken outbuildings loosely grouped, with few fences or boundaries, around rectangular halls built of large posts. During the first three Anglo-Saxon centuries, these were often rebuilt on slightly different sites within their more enduring field systems, so that they almost seemed to drift across the landscape. Recent environmental archaeology has suggested that, although loss of the demand for agricultural products from the Roman army and the towns reduced the intensity of farming effort, in fertile regions like that around Blewbury and the Astons, there was little disruption in the routine of rural life at the end of the Roman period. Some farmers may have turned more to cattle and sheep, or chosen not to utilise their least-favoured land, but the countryside was still well exploited.

THE BLEWBURY CHARTER

With farming continuing essentially unchanged in many areas until the ninth century, the boundaries of different estates and field layouts could have persisted from the Romano-British period or even earlier. This is difficult to prove, and much discussed, but while farm buildings shifted and were rebuilt, the sensible components of agricultural estates were less likely to alter. Fortunately, there is a tenth century Anglo-Saxon charter for Blewbury, with an unusually detailed description of the boundaries of a large grant of land from King Edmund to Bishop Aelfric. Such charters did not refer to maps, but the boundary clause in this 944AD document walks the reader in vivid prose from ditch to thorn tree to pagan burial place in a clockwise perambulation of what are now more-or-less the outer boundaries of the amalgamated parishes of Blewbury, the two Moretons, Aston Upthorpe and Aston Tirrold.

The charter recorded what had existed for perhaps centuries; such a large composite estate could have had a long history of amalgamation and fragmentation. Indeed the central position of the hillfort raises the suspicion that tenth century words perpetuated a prehistoric territory. Standing at the top of Woodway, at the edge of the Downs south of Blewbury, the northern view takes in most of the old estate, with all the vital agricultural elements clearly on offer: pasture, arable land, watercourses and meadow. Although the estate was divided up under later Anglo-Saxon pressure to create smaller land units it survived, as recorded in Domesday, as the Blewbury Hundred, or administrative and judicial unit, with Blewbury as its centre. That Blewbury's Domesday status reflected a position acquired over some time is revealed by the names of the other villages, which mark them out as subsidiary settlements: Aston meaning 'estate east of Blewbury' and Moreton 'the estate in marshy land'.

Saint Birinus preaching. Part of a window in All Saints Church, Aston Upthorpe.

The Church and Politics

Part of Blewbury's significance by 1086AD may have been due to its development around an important minster church, founded as early as the mid seventh century under the stimulus of the missionary activities of Birinus, who reached this area around 633AD. By then the thriving kingdom of Wessex counted Blewbury within its reach, despite the predatory interest of the developing Mercian power just to the north of the Thames. Through the seventh and eighth centuries, the north and west of former Berkshire were disputed between Wessex and Mercia. When fighting erupted out of failed alliances, arranged marriages and tribute deals, it was probably small-scale and localised; nonetheless, these now-peaceful acres were, even before the Vikings came, potential royal skirmishing grounds. The baptism of Wessex's King Cynegils by Birinus, virtually on the border with pagan Mercia, and in the supporting presence of powerful Northumbrian King Oswald, was an aggressive political statement as well as a boost to the spread of Christianity. In c.635AD Cynegils gave Dorchester to Birinus as the episcopal seat of his new see, and minster churches began to flourish across the area, even though, only a few years later, the threat of Mercian expansion prompted a relocation of the see to Winchester.

Early minster churches were more like later monastic communities than parish churches and had considerable social and economic influence over the surrounding district. They became new centres of activity, not only because of their religious role but because they ran their own estates and attracted traders and craftsmen to their gates. We do not know exactly when Blewbury's church was founded but it is recorded in Domesday as a minster church; we can speculate that it was also an early minster and played a crucial part in the village's rise to prominence.

Christianity and a literate administration were implicated in wide-ranging changes in later Anglo-Saxon times, when early kingdoms gave way to fewer, more bureaucratic ones. By the ninth century, farmland was under pressure from ecclesiastical overlords, the holders of new, smaller estates, and increased trading. Villages began to consolidate around their churches, built by the local minor lord or thegn, their unstructured wanderings across the landscape were abandoned and new, more productive agricultural methods were adopted. Inhabitants combined to farm large open fields around the village, exploiting other land in common. The excavations at Yarnton show that, by this time, the locals were protecting their meadows and manuring their fields, indicating changing agricultural practices. Descriptions in Blewbury's charter imply that the fields around the village were already worked in this fashion and the framework for the present landscape was being established.

So the religious, social and economic changes of the Saxon period gradually transformed the lives of ordinary farming folk. But the concerns of kings and nobles also influenced their lives. In the early Anglo-Saxon years, nearby Dorchester had kept enough of its character as a regional centre to win the honour of being Birinus' see. In the tenth century Abingdon enjoyed its moment of ecclesiastical attention when reforming bishop Aethelwold took on the declining Abbey and transformed it into the model monastic community for his ongoing crusade. For a while Abingdon was the foremost religious house in the kingdom. Royalty still paid their calls and on one memorable and less high-minded occasion it is solemnly recounted that mead mugs

RICHARD HOOK

miraculously refilled rendering King Eadred's retinue royally drunk. Blewbury itself may not have been at the epicentre of these momentous events but the reverberations surely reached the village.

A number of local non-ecclesiastical sites have been suggested as royal manors where the itinerant court stopped to dispense justice and avail itself of the food and services due from the estates. Drayton, Sutton Courtenay and Long Wittenham are all contenders, on the basis of aerial photographs and chance finds; Blewbury, as a focal village and hundred centre, may itself have been a royal manor but the evidence is not conclusive. Once again the village seemed to hover slightly on the periphery.

Perhaps the peak of Blewbury Hundred's entanglement with royal politics came in the ninth century. Tradition has it that critical encounters between King Aethelred, his more famous brother Alfred, and the land-seeking Viking Great Army happened on the Downs to the south of Blewbury (see Battle of Ashdown). Even if the exact location is disputed it would not be surprising that significant clashes occurred in the area. We have already seen the region passing between Mercia and Wessex. This pattern continued with the early ninth century conquests of Offa of Mercia, and then the return of Wessex's sovereignty by the mid century, sustained until the Norman Conquest. Thus it was an army of Wessex that faced the Danes at Ashdown in 871AD in the battle for the Thames and the rich lands to the south. Probably men from Blewbury and its surrounds were among the ranks of fyrdmen (the local noble's men, required to line up with him in battle) pitched against the Danes. Wherever the battle was fought, local families may have lost men to the fighting, goods to the needs of their army or Danish raiding, and lived in fear of what the outcome might bring.

After this passing success of 871AD, and many encounters in battle and various reverses later, by 878AD Alfred had secured the survival of Wessex and contained the Danes in the north and east of the country. The next century was one of economic expansion and the development of towns, a period that decided the balance of power in the region. Wallingford and, in particular, Oxford were beginning to flourish as towns, having been chosen by Alfred and his son as the fortified market centres of the crucial Thames corridor. Just to the west of Wallingford,

RICHARD HOOK

Blewbury began to settle into its place as a notable, and venerable, but minor player in the development of the region.

JANE HARRISON

SELECTED REFERENCES AND FURTHER READING
1. BLAIR, J. 1994 ANGLO-SAXON OXFORDSHIRE, SUTTON.
2. BLAIR, J. 2005 THE CHURCH IN ANGLO-SAXON SOCIETY, OXFORD UNIVERSITY PRESS.
3. BOYLE, A, A. DODD, D. MILES AND A. MUDD 1995 TWO OXFORDSHIRE CEMETERIES: BERINSFIELD AND DIDCOT, THAMES VALLEY MONOGRAPH NO. 8, OXFORD ARCHAEOLOGICAL UNIT.
4. COOK, J. AND T ROWLEY (EDS) 1986 THE ARCHAEOLOGY OF THE OXFORD REGION, OXFORD UNIVERSITY DEPARTMENT FOR EXTERNAL STUDIES.
5. FORD, S. 1987 EAST BERKSHIRE ARCHAEOLOGICAL SURVEY, BERKSHIRE COUNTY COUNCIL.
6. PEAKE, H. 1931 THE ARCHAEOLOGY OF BERKSHIRE, METHUEN.
7. ROWLEY, T. (ED) 1974 ANGLO-SAXON SETTLEMENT AND LANDSCAPE, B.A.R. BRITISH SERIES NO. 6.
8. GELLING, M. 1976 THE PLACE NAMES OF BERKSHIRE, ENGLISH PLACE-NAME SOCIETY, VOL. LI, (AND OTHER BOOKS BY THE SAME AUTHOR).
9. HEY, G. 2004 YARNTON: SAXON AND MEDIEVAL SETTLEMENT AND LANDSCAPE, THAMES VALLEY LANDSCAPES MONOGRAPH NO. 20, OXFORD ARCHAEOLOGY.
10. YORKE, B. (ED) 1997 BISHOP AETHELWOLD: HIS CAREER AND INFLUENCE, BOYDELL PRESS.

Shadows on the Landscape
Recent Archaeological Discoveries

© Crown copyright, courtesy of the photographic section, RAF Benson

Part III: Romano-British Period (AD43 to AD410)

The defences on Blewburton would have rapidly become obsolete once the Roman invasion took place. In terms of scale, this was a minor defended site, and it is likely that Romanisation took place in this area through politics and negotiation rather than overt and widespread violence. The archaeological evidence suggests that many of the indigenous Iron Age farming families and settlements in our study area flourished as never before. The extensive investigations in the Clay Vale (Hearne 2000 and various unpublished reports ibid.) have shown that during this period, much of the land previously occupied by settlements that were apparently deserted in the 5th to 3rd centuries BC was re-colonised, and some completely new settlements were established on previously unexploited land. Agrarian activities expanded with renewed vigour, and while there appears to have been some "restructuring" in the 2nd century AD, many settlements continued to expand into the late 4th

The Hill from the South West. The road to the top and gateway remain where they were in the Iron Age. The 6th Century Saxon cemetery is within the Iron Age fort on top to the right of the gateway.

The Hill from the North

The most prominent earthworks on the Hill today are the parallel terraces around the western end. These are the strip-lynchets (agricultural terraces), which are thought to be of medieval origin but could possibly be much earlier. Above these sit the remains of defensive ramparts of the Iron Age – now much eroded by subsequent work and damage by rabbits. Baldon Hill can be seen at the top right, where an important, and possibly early Christian, burial was found recently.

and early 5th centuries AD.

By the 4th century AD a number of these farming settlements had coalesced into complexes more than 5 hectares in size, with fields, enclosures and track ways extending over one and a half kilometres. It is possible that the land between these settlements could have been managed as "common" grazing by neighbouring farms.

By this time some of these larger settlements also boasted small "cottage villas". Although not of high status, these families could flaunt some luxury items such as bronze dishes and accessories made of decorated Kimmeridge shale [13], as well as the extravagance of occasional centrally heated rooms and unsophisticated mosaic floors. The investigations on land west of Didcot [16] have produced a very similar story, with a 1st century AD settlement around Zulu Farm, and a larger, mainly 2nd to late 4th century settlement complete with small cottage villa on the hilltop further north.

As mentioned previously, the site at the Rutherford Appleton Laboratory also produced evidence of a Romano-British farmstead [10]. The early Roman farm appears to have been an enclosed settlement. By the middle of the Roman period the range of pottery suggests fairly wide trade links, but there are no other indicators to suggest any special status. Two cremation burials were found from this period. By the later Roman period, the site appears to have shifted slightly, while the discovery of a corn drier emphasises the continuing agrarian nature of the farm. Fragments of a possible building and a single human burial also came to light, and the quantity of pottery suggests that the farm flourished into the second half of the 4th century AD.

At the gas pipeline site west of Brightwell-cum-Sotwell, [18] the early Roman period saw a rapid expansion of the late Iron Age agrarian system with large curvilinear enclosures and field ditches, although it is clear that by now the actual settlement has shifted and we are looking at the agricultural hinterland. But several burials placed in both dug graves, and in the fills of abandoned ditches, suggest that a settlement continued not too far away. This agricultural land falls into disuse by the start of the fifth century, and probably remained fallow until the medieval period.

Birmingham Archaeology investigated land north of the Wallingford Road at Didcot, in 2004, [7] and found yet another low status Roman farming settlement, typical in character to those linear settlements recently identified over much of the clay vale. Numerous shallow irregular pits left after tree felling and stump removal, indicate a phase of woodland clearance in the late prehistoric or early Roman periods. This farm may have been abandoned as the changing drainage pattern of the Thames, caused or at least exacerbated by the removal of forest cover, and soil erosion by ploughing, resulted in seasonal flooding. By the late Roman period, a thick layer of alluvium covered parts of the site, and the inhabitants probably moved to higher ground on Hadden Hill, where we know a later Roman settlement exists. These fields were subsequently known as East Hagbourne Marsh.

This period of rapid agrarian expansion is also mirrored on the chalk downs, where, until a few decades ago, the extensive earthworks of mainly late Iron Age and Romano-British farms and field systems were visible everywhere. The vast majority of these remains have since been ploughed out, and their ghosts can now be seen only from the air as crop and soil marks. The recent pipeline that crossed this area produced evidence of only a few very shallow boundary ditches heavily truncated by ploughing.

EARLY SAXON (FIFTH TO SIXTH CENTURY AD)

New colonisers, bringing a very different culture, rapidly followed the economic breakdown of the early post Roman period in this area. 5th century Saxon pottery is found on late Roman sites, and by the 6th century AD, Saxon settlements were strongly embedded. As we have seen, there was a sizeable 6th century Saxon cemetery within the ramparts of Blewburton Hill, but until very recently other material evidence of this period was relatively sparse.

The Transco pipeline project [18] produced evidence from the Saxon period that is closely connected with Blewburton Hill. South of the A417, on the west-facing slope of Baldon Hill, the archaeologists found a single burial. The grave contained the skeleton of a young adult aged about 16-20 years at death, lying with the head to the west. Unfortunately the skull of the skeleton was missing, presumably ripped out by the plough. Slight traces of ridge and furrow may indicate medieval ploughing, and the field is currently under arable cultivation. This undoubtedly accounts for the poor condition of the bones. The burial was clearly of early Saxon date and the grave goods included a typical small, narrow-bladed iron knife, an iron key or girdle-hanger that would have been worn on the hip, and a possible iron spoon bowl. Other small iron wire fragments may have formed a long chain. In addition to these normal Saxon artefacts was a copper alloy leaf-shaped seal-box base of Roman date (probably 2nd century or later), and a rare copper alloy circular openwork belt-fitting with a simple geometric design of intersecting cross and circle.

This last object is extremely important; for it is a type of Frankish artefact that first appears in sixth century Rhineland cemeteries. Only a few have been found in southern and eastern England. The earliest datable English examples are present in Early Saxon burials of the first half of the sixth century, but appear to have continued on well into the seventh-century. As the calibrated radiocarbon date for the Blewbury burial is AD 680 to 880, this suggests that the most likely date for the burial is the second half of the seventh century. [S. Tyler in 18]

This dating raises interesting possibilities about the nature of this burial, for the body was aligned west-east (a preferred orientation among 7th century burials) and the grave-goods are modest for a Pagan burial. If it does date to between 650 and 700 it lies within the early period of Christianisation begun by St Birinus in 635. Tyler (ibid) suggests that this may be "a Christian burial but harking back to Pagan traditions"). If it is not Pagan, then it is the first Christian Saxon burial to be discovered at Blewbury. However, it is likely that the transition from Pagan to entirely Christian burial practices was a slow and complex one, and we cannot be certain of its religious origins.

Here our narrative ends, but there are always new questions to be asked, and current investigations are taking place literally as this piece is being written. For instance, building work in 2005 off the A417 at Harwell revealed a single burial with an iron knife (Hugh Coddington, personal communication). This could be Saxon, and as I write this, the remains are being analysed. Until that is completed, this individual will remain just another fleeting shadow on the landscape. Future work will further enliven the rich and complex history of the environs of Blewburton Hill, and illuminate those past lives that inhabited and moulded the landscape we now take for granted.

PAUL SMITH
OXFORDSHIRE COUNTY ARCHAEOLOGIST.

REFERENCE LIST FOR SHADOWS ON THE LANDSCAPE PARTS I, II & III:

1. ANDERSON, E. ET AL 2003. NEWBURY REINFORCEMENT PIPELINE. POST-EXCAVATION ASSESSMENT AND UPDATED PROJECT DESIGN. OXFORD ARCHAEOLOGY. [UNPUBLISHED REPORT]

2. BARBER, A. & THOMAS, A. 1998. ABINGDON RESERVOIR PROPOSALS, OXON 1997. ARCHAEOLOGICAL EVALUATION (VOL. 1&2). COTSWOLD ARCHAEOLOGICAL TRUST [UNPUBLISHED REPORT]

3. BARBER, A. & THOMAS, A. 1998. ABINGDON RESERVOIR PROPOSALS. ARCHAEOLOGICAL EVALUATION SITES 406 & 412 COTSWOLD ARCHAEOLOGICAL TRUST [UNPUBLISHED REPORT]

4. BARRETT, J. 1980. THE EVOLUTION OF LATER BRONZE AGE SETTLEMENT IN THE BRITISH LATER BRONZE AGE PART I (ED. J. BARRETT & R. BRADLEY) BAR BRITISH SERIES 83(1)

5. BOYLE, A. & MUDD, A. 1995. AN ANGLO SAXON CEMETERY AT DIDCOT POWER STATION IN TWO OXFORDSHIRE ANGLO-SAXON CEMETERIES: BERINSFIELD AND DIDCOT.(A BOYLE ET AL) THAMES VALLEY LANDSCAPES MONOGRAPH NO.8. OXFORD ARCHAEOLOGICAL UNIT. 201-253

6. THOMAS, A. 1998. ARCHAEOLOGICAL EVALUATION. COTSWOLD ARCHAEOLOGICAL TRUST [UNPUBLISHED REPORT]

7. DUNCAN, M. & JONES, L. 2004. LAND NORTH OF THE A4130, DIDCOT, OXFORDSHIRE

8. (LADYGROVE EAST): ARCHAEOLOGICAL EVALUATION 2004. [UNPUBLISHED REPORT]

9. GRAY JONES, 2002. AN ARCHAEOLOGICAL EVALUATION AT RUTHERFORD APPLETON LABORATORY. [UNPUBLISHED REPORT]

10. GRAY JONES, 2003. ARCHAEOLOGICAL INVESTIGATION AT THE BLUE CAR PARK EXTENSION, RUTHERFORD APPLETON LABORATORY, CHILTON, OXON. [UNPUBLISHED REPORT]

11. HALL, M. 1994. SOUTH WEST OXON RESERVOIR PROPOSAL. AN ARCHAEOLOGICAL EVALUATION OF SITE 110 THAMES VALLEY ARCHAEOLOGICAL SERVICES [UNPUBLISHED REPORT]

12. HARDY, A. 1997. ABINGDON RESERVOIR PROPOSAL, ABINGDON, OXON: ARCHAEOLOGICAL EVALUATION REPORT – C13A (VOL. 1&2) OXFORD ARCHAEOLOGICAL UNIT [UNPUBLISHED REPORT]

13. HEARNE, C. M. 2000. ARCHAEOLOGICAL EVALUATION IN THE VALE OF WHITE HORSE, NEAR ABINGDON, 1992 – 99. OXONIENSIA LXV 7-12

14. HINGLEY, R. 1985. LOCATION, FUNCTION AND STATUS: A ROMANO-BRITISH RELIGIOUS COMPLEX AT THE NOAH'S ARK INN, FRILFORD, OXFORDSHIRE. OXFORD JOURNAL OF ARCHAEOLOGY 4. 201-214.

15. JOHNS, R. 1998. ABINGDON RESERVOIR PROPOSAL, ABINGDON, OXON: ARCHAEOLOGICAL EVALUATION REPORT SITES 400 & 417. OXFORD ARCHAEOLOGICAL UNIT [UNPUBLISHED REPORT]

16. MASEFIELD, R. 2002. AN ARCHAEOLOGICAL EVALUATION AT DIDCOT WEST, FIELDS 21-23. [UNPUBLISHED REPORT]

17. MOORE, J. & PARSONS, G. 2004. ARCHAEOLOGICAL WATCHING BRIEF DIAMOND BUILDING PROJECT, RUTHERFORD APPLETON LABORATORY, CHILTON, OXON. [UNPUBLISHED REPORT]18. NETWORK ARCHAEOLOGY 2005. CHALGROVE TO EAST ILSLEY GAS PIPELINE: ARCHAEOLOGICAL WATCHING BRIEF AND EXCAVATIONS. DRAFT REPORT [UNPUBLISHED REPORT]

19. RPS, 2001. DIDCOT WEST. DETAILED WALKOVER SURVEY AND FIELDWALKING RESULTS. [UNPUBLISHED REPORT]

20. RPS, 2004. GREAT WESTERN PARK DIDCOT, SUPPLEMENT TO ENVIRONMENTAL STATEMENT CHAPTER 8 & REVISED FIGS. 8.1 – 8.9

21. RUBEN, I. & FORD, S. ET AL 1992. ARCHAEOLOGICAL EXCAVATIONS AT WALLINGFORD ROAD DIDCOT, SOUTH OXFORDSHIRE, 1991. OXONIENSIA LVII 1992, 1-28

22. STANSBIE, D. ET AL 2004. EXCAVATIONS AT THE NEWBURY REINFORCEMENT PIPELINE: IRON AGE – ROMAN ACTIVITY AND A NEOLITHIC PIT GROUP. OXFORD ARCHAEOLOGY. [UNPUBLISHED REPORT]

23. THOMAS, A. 1998. ARCHAEOLOGICAL EVALUATION. COTSWOLD ARCHAEOLOGICAL TRUST [UNPUBLISHED REPORT]

24. WEAVER, STEVEN D.G. 1996. SOUTH WEST OXON RESERVOIR PROPOSAL. AN ARCHAEOLOGICAL EVALUATION OF SITE 126 SOUTH. THAMES VALLEY ARCHAEOLOGICAL SERVICES [UNPUBLISHED REPORT]

25. WEAVER, STEVEN D.G. 1998. ABINGDON RESERVOIR PROPOSAL. AN ARCHAEOLOGICAL EVALUATION OF SITE 126 NORTH (VOL. 1) AND SITE197 (VOL. 2) THAMES VALLEY ARCHAEOLOGICAL SERVICES [UNPUBLISHED REPORT]

The Vikings are attacking from the right. Alfred (later "the Great") is on the left with his Saxon soldiers. The Saxon King Ethelred, Alfred's brother, is arriving late at the top left of the picture.

Anglo Saxon Chronicler Asser tells us that "... there was a thorn tree of stunted growth ... around this tree the opponents came together with loud shouts from all sides ..."

THE BATTLE OF ASHDOWN
8 JANUARY 871

The inhabitants of Aston Upthorpe have long held that the Saxon King Ethelred, elder brother to Alfred the Great, spent the night before the Battle of Ashdown camped on nearby Blewburton Hill. They claim that Ethelred heard mass in the church of All Saints in Aston Upthorpe on the morning of the battle and, refusing to leave before the priest had finished, was late in arriving for the battle, forcing Alfred his younger brother, to attack the Danes without him

Four days before the battle of Ashdown, the Saxon army had had a major skirmish at Reading. The Anglo Saxon Chronicler Asser writes:

"... this year the pagan [Viking] army came to Reading and in the course of three nights afterwards were met by Alderman Ethelwulf [A local Saxon chieftain] at Englefield where he fought them and obtained a victory. About four nights after this King Ethelred and Alfred his brother led the army to Reading where they fought the enemy and there was much slaughter on either hand. Alderman Ethelwulf being among the slain but the Danes kept possession of the field."

Afterwards the Saxons withdrew, probably to somewhere in the Wallingford area. Saxon spies had no doubt spotted the Danish army on the move once again from their camp at Reading and the alert to arms had gone out. What better place for an army to camp than on the fortified hilltop of Blewburton Hill?

A SAXON VICTORY

King Ethelred chose a great vantage point on the top of Blewburton Hill and could spot an army on the move coming from the north a long way off. Also, according to local legend, Alfred spent the night before the battle camped on Kingstanding Hill, located near the start of the Fair Mile and clearly visible from Blewburton Hill. Between them Alfred and Ethelred had the area covered and were well prepared.

The Danes had probably taken their men from Reading by boat to Streatley and then, keeping to the high ground, marched along the ancient Ridgeway path. By nightfall on the evening before the battle, the Danish army were probably camped on the hill to the south of Kingstanding Hill just across the steep v-shaped valley from Alfred's men. Asser writes that:

"... the pagans divided themselves into two bodies, and began to prepare defenses ... which the Christians perceiving divided their army also into two troops and also begun defenses."

A line of ancient earthworks called Devils Ditch, cuts across the track leading up to Unhill Woods onto Moulsford Downs. Were these the hurriedly thrown up front line defenses for either a Viking or Saxon army camp whilst they rested there the night before the battle?

At dawn on January 8th 871, Alfred marched his men to the battlefield site from Kingstanding Hill along the Fairmile, leading half the King's army. By following the ancient Fairmile as it gradually converges with the Ridgeway, Alfred kept ahead of the Danes since he did not dare to allow the Danish army to move past him towards Wantage. The other half of the Saxon army were, according to local folklore, still camped with King Ethelred on Blewburton Hill.

Alfred arrived at a key position on the Ridgeway just south of Lowbury Hill ahead of the enemy, thus blocking the approaching Danish army, and took up a stand lower down the slope waiting for King Ethelred and his men to join him.

Asser tells us:

"Now the Christians had determined that King Ethelred with his men should attack the two pagan kings, but that his brother Alfred with his troops should take the chance of war against the Earls. Things being so arranged, the King remained in prayer and the pagans came up rapidly to fight. Then Alfred, though possessing a subordinate authority, could no longer support the troops of the enemy, unless he retreated or charged upon them without waiting for his brother. At length he bravely led his troops against the hostile army as they had before arranged, but without waiting for his brothers arrival."

Asser continues: "forming his men into a dense phalanx, he

marched on at once to meet the foe. The field of battle was not equally advantageous to both parties, the Pagans occupied the higher ground, and the Christians came up from below."

The battle started without King Ethelred. Alfred sent an urgent message that his brother must come at once or the battle would be lost. Ethelred insisted on finishing hearing mass, and then departed with his troops to join Alfred. It was his arrival that turned the day in favour of the Saxons.

The Anglo Saxon chronicler, Robert of Gloucester, wrote the only contemporary account of the day. Asser wrote his account of the battle in more detail but twenty years after the event. He made much of the outcome of the Battle as being a great victory for the Saxons and especially for Alfred. Indeed it was a Saxon victory, one of the very few amongst dozens of skirmishes and battles fought over a period of several years.

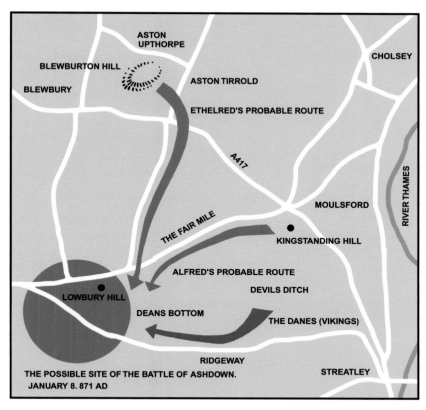

The Vikings were heading west from Streatley towards Wantage. Alfred was forced to attack near Lowbury Hill before Ethelred arrived.

SITE OF THE BATTLE

Historians have long disputed the site of this historic battle. But recently, whilst not actually pinpointing the exact location, opinion strongly supports the theory of it having being fought within three miles of Blewburton Hill on the high ground where the Ridgeway passes to the south of Lowbury Hill.

The Complete Guide to the Battlefields of Britain, by David Smurthwaite, confirms that the site of Ashdown has long been disputed. Several attempts have been made to pinpoint it and many accounts written, which place it as widely apart as Ashbury in the Vale of the White Horse to the west and Ashdown in Sussex to the

South. However, as Smurthwaite's book remarks, these have mostly been discredited in favour of the site near Lowbury Hill, within easy striking distance of Blewburton Hill. In confirmation of its recently recognised status, several new road Atlases have the battlefield clearly marked with the date 871 on Aston Downs.

ASTON'S INVOLVEMENT

The oral testimony of one local village has stuck rigorously to this story of King Ethelred. Oral history, by its very nature, cannot be verified, but the first written account to appear in Aston Upthorpe was in 1830. It was written by the children of the then resident Presbyterian Minister of Aston Tirrold and seems to have relied mainly on local accounts. In their acknowledgements however, the Marris children referred to this story as having been noted in *Hume's History of England*. David Hume's work was first published in 1754 and also places the battlefield near Lowbury Hill. From where did Hume get his evidence? His book does not reference his sources. Both these accounts pre-date the large volume of work, *The Victorian History of Berkshire*, and *To the Ascendune Battlefield* published in 1894 by Henry Taunt.

It is worth noting that no other village in this vicinity, that could have claimed to be near the battlefield, recounts the same or similar story of the King at prayer. The villages of Compton and Ilsley also claim an historical connection with the actual battlefield. In Asser's account of the battle he writes: "...there was a thorn tree of stunted growth... around this tree the opponents came together with loud shouts from all sides".

Compton was in the old and now defunct hundred of Nachededorne, which means "the naked thorn" – hence Compton's claim.

East Ilsley also claims to have had a tree upon Thorn Down, (near where a church was later built) around which the battle was supposed to have raged. The name Ilsley is thought to derive from the ancient Saxon Hilde-Laege, meaning place of conflict.

In Asser's account he writes, of the Danish army, "five earls were slain together with many thousand pagans covering with their bodies the whole plain of Ashdune".

One wonders if there still remains some evidence somewhere up

"...A sea-folk blinder than the sea
Broke all about this land,
But Alfred up against them bare
And gripped the ground and grasped the
air,
Staggered, and strove to stand.

He bent them back with spear and
spade,
With desperate dyke and wall,
With foemen leaning on his shield
And roaring on him when he reeled;
And no help came at all..."

*From "The Ballad of the Whitehorse"
by G.K.Chesterton (1874-1936)*

Alfred at the Battle of Ashdown.

near the Ridgeway of the many thousands of pagan and Saxon bodies left after the battle?

Another rather "romantic" interpretation is that Deans Bottom, which runs to the east of Lowbury Hill, may be a possible corruption of Danes Bottom because the Danes ran away after the battle and were slain in their thousands in the gully! (Ref: Henry Taunt 1894.)

The scene of this battleground spread out across many square miles of downland. Therefore the consequences of this one event would have impacted on all three of the parishes of Compton, Ilsley and Aston Upthorpe. The story of such a momentous occasion would have passed down the annals of history to modern times in the surrounding area. Hence all three parishes have a claim to have played their part in the battle of Ashdown.

The 1883 Ordnance Survey map of Blewburton Hill marks the hill incorrectly as a "Danish Camp" .On this map there is mention of military weapons and human remains having been dug up between Blewbury and Aston Tirrold near the modern A 417. These "remains" relate to Saxon finds and there is evidence of several other Saxon burials around this area. Also there has been a find of a Scandinavian weapon of the right period discovered upon the Downs not far from the alleged Ashdown battlefield site (ref Paul Smith, Oxfordshire County Archaeologist)

The other strong claimant to the Ashdown battlefield site is the White Horse Hill beyond Wantage. So where exactly was Ashdown? The whole ridge of The Berkshire Downs from an area to the west of Streatley to Ashbury in the east seems to be referred to as "Ashdown". Michael Wood, in his book "In search of Domesday", writes, " the first glance one gets of Ashdown is the high misty ridges to the south as you get off the train at Didcot."

Pre-Norman records referring to the name Ashdown are first mentioned in a grant of land to Cenwalh in 648 of three thousand hides of "high land" called Aescendune to his nephew Cuthred. In a later entry, Eadred is said to have given some hides of land at Cumptune (Compton) near the hill called Aescendune.

After their victory Asser notes: "the whole pagan army pursued its flight, not only until night but until the next day until they reached the stronghold from which they had sullied" [Reading].

If the battle site had been The White Horse Hill, it is unlikely that the defeated Danish army could have returned to their Reading camp (about forty miles) in just one night and part of the next day. The distance from our supposed site of the battle to the Danish camp at Reading, by the shortest route for someone walking, is about 16 miles.

All these references help narrow down the spot of the battlefield to an area north of Compton, high up on the Downs within a short march of Reading. This is mainly why the experts have arrived at the conclusion that the main battlefield area is located about half a mile south of Lowbury Hill, on a wide area of several square miles bisected by the ancient Ridgeway path.

One final concluding piece of evidence about the Ashdown battlefield site is included in the Anglo Saxon Chronicles (Richard of Gloucester) written for the year 1006.

"The Vikings under Sweyn the Dane, came in their ships after Martinmas via the Isle of Wight through Hampshire and Berkshire observing their ancient custom of lighting beacons as they went. After Reading they followed the Thames to Wallingford which they burnt and looted. They then went by Cholsey up to the Downs where they marched in triumph past the site of their former defeat of Aescendune before turning south across the Kennet and making their way back to the sea with all their plunder."

Asser and the other Anglo Saxon Chroniclers are unlikely to be a truly reliable source. But are 1,135 years of local oral testimony so much less reliable? King Ethelred may well have spent a night on the hill top fort at Blewburton the day before the Battle of Ashdown, that January morning in 871. So when next you look out over the rolling countryside from the top of this hill, think of King Ethelred and the Battle of Ashdown.

JUDY BARRADELL-SMITH
ASTONS HISTORY GROUP

ACKNOWLEDGEMENT
THE WORK OF ELPHIN LLOYD-JONES IN CREATING THE MAP OF THE PROBABLE BATTLEFIELD IS GRATEFULLY ACKNOWLEDGED. SOME INFORMATION ON THE MAP WAS REPRODUCED BY PERMISSION OF ORDNANCE SURVEY ON BEHALF OF HMSO © CROWN 2006 LICENSE NO. 100045986

SAINT BIRINUS, BISHOP OF WESSEX
BORN: C.600 DIED: 3RD DECEMBER 649

Every year Blewbury attracts Christians from many parishes, both from within the Diocese and beyond, for a pilgrimage to Dorchester Abbey on the first Sunday in July. The object of this pilgrimage is to mark the importance of this area for the advent of Christianity in the ancient region of Wessex. Myth, legend, history and fact are inextricably bound together in the story of St. Birinus and Cynegils, the king of Wessex.

The facts are well documented. Birinus was consecrated bishop by Archbishop Asterius in Genoa in the 7th century AD and sent to England by Pope Honorius I in 634 AD to convert the people of Mercia to the north of this area. The Venerable Bede records that, on arriving first in the northern part of Wessex, he decided that his evangelistic zeal could be put to better use converting the pagans in this area. (Plus ça change, plus c'est la meme chose).

It is here that legend seems to take over. King Cynegils, intent on hearing the good bishop out, chose Churn Knob, above Blewbury, for the meeting. This pagan burial mound could have been a significant spot for important events, perched as it is above the Thames valley. Impressed by Birinus' missionary fervour he consented to baptism, which was carried out in the Thames near Dorchester. Cynegils gave Birinus a parcel of land at Dorchester as a thanks offering, where the bishop built his cathedral (Dorchester Abbey) and became the first bishop of the new see of Wessex. Birinus was instrumental in the foundation of Winchester Cathedral and after his death it is alleged that his successor, as Bishop of Winchester, had Birinus' remains moved there. His shrine at Dorchester is the focus for the annual pilgrimage and is in the process of restoration.

The facts surrounding the conversion and baptism of Cynegils

(Above): St. Michael's Church, Blewbury; (Top right): Dorchester Abbey window c.1250 AD, thought to depict Birinus being consecrated by Archbishop Asterius in Genoa before he was sent to England by Pope Honorius I in 634 AD to convert the people of Mercia.

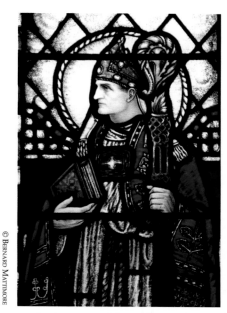

are more prosaic. It is doubtful that he was baptised immediately following Birinus' sermon. The king was intent on marrying the daughter of King Oswald of Northumbria, thus cementing an important alliance to oppose the Mercian threat.

Oswald, as a Christian, was reluctant to deal with a pagan. St. Birinus was summoned to king Cynegil's conference at Bracknell in order to put an end to the impasse. Thus Cynegils became a Christian at Bracknell, not in the Thames at Dorchester, proving that fact is sometimes less romantic than fiction. However, this does not detract from the effectiveness of the good bishop, who richly deserves the special windows portraying him in St. Michael's Church in Blewbury and All Saints Church in Aston Upthorpe as well as in the impressive abbey church at Dorchester.

Evidence for the foundation of the myth surrounding the baptism of Cynegils comes from the historical account of an episode that followed Birinus' intervention at Bracknell. Some members of the royal court were anxious to see where Birinus was to build his cathedral and travelled north to Dorchester. It is said that many of them, wishing to become Christians, were baptised in the Thames at the river crossing at Brightwell. Since the Thames does not run through the present day Brightwell, the site of the baptism could be near Little Wittenham. This may be something for the modern day pilgrims to think about as they wearily cross the river at Day's Lock, and serve to boost their energy for the last mile to Dorchester and the end of their pilgrimage.

CANON EDWIN CLEMENTS

ACKNOWLEDGEMENTS
PERMISSION FROM THE RECTOR OF DORCHESTER ABBEY, REVEREND SUE BOOYS, TO TAKE PHOTOGRAPHS OF THE STAINED GLASS WINDOWS IN THE ABBEY, IS GRATEFULLY ACKNOWLEDGED.

(Top left): Detail from the St Birinus window in All Saints' Church, Aston Upthorpe and (right): A Victorian depiction of the saint, 1887, in the Nave of Dorchester Abbey

THE DOMESDAY BOOK:
BLEWBURY HUNDRED

© READING MUSEUM SERVICE

The last scene of the Bayeux Tapestry showing the Normans driving the English from the battlefield at Hastings 1066.

AFTER THE NORMAN CONQUEST

William overwhelmed Harold's army near Hastings on 14th October 1066, the violent conquest of an old established culture, by a young, brutal and warlike state. The twenty years following the conquest were a time of terrible trauma for the people of England. Plundering bands of armed and ruthless men quartered the land. Plague, cattle disease, crop failure and bad weather were frequently added to the torment of a hapless, but still resilient and resourceful, population. To make matters worse, William's principal aim was to extract as much tax as possible from the conquered nation to fund his military objectives in Wales, Scotland and France, while keeping the English in subjection and opposing the Danes. Already imposing cruel and indiscriminate taxation, he ordered the compilation of the Domesday Book in 1085 as a means of further increasing it. The book attempted, with varied success, to detail the value of every corner of the land and the person responsible for it, before and after the conquest. The Berkshire area was well covered. The Shire Courts, amidst this terrible misery, sat before the King's commissioners, under oath, to detail the assets under their jurisdiction. To make sure of accuracy the process was repeated by different officers to discover deception and denounce miscreants to the King. The name Domesday implied just that; like The Day of Judgment, its decisions were final.

But Domesday was about more than tax. An efficient, powerful monarch wanted to know as much as possible about his holdings and crucially the land wealth of his nobles (and everyone else). In land lay power and influence: William used Domesday to understand the power relations and social complexities of his new kingdom and to record the immense changes in ownership following the upheaval of the Conquest.

Despite the dreadful context of its creation, the Domesday Book provides a unique and extraordinary record of the English counties more than nine hundred years ago and we can but marvel at the detail it reveals. The Blewbury Hundred was no exception and we have a rich picture of the area in 1086. The entries for the Hundred make fascinating reading, but to appreciate them fully we need to understand something of the fabric of feudal society.

ADMINISTRATIVE ORGANIZATION

The Domesday Book was compiled in less than a year. Ironically this was only possible because of the remarkably efficient system of local government set up by the West Saxon Kings during the tenth century. England was divided into shires and the shires into hundreds. A Hundred (about 100 hides) was an administrative subdivision of the Shire with fiscal, judicial and military functions. The free men of the Hundred met monthly in the Hundred Court to conduct local business and settle disputes. The Shire Court met twice yearly and, amongst other vital matters, dealt with royal taxes and military service. The King's representative, the Earl, and the Bishop presided. During proceedings the sheriff (shire-reeve), the King's chief judicial and financial officer, would have faced other reeves representing local interests, particularly those of noblemen. Arguments must have been frequent, passionate and bitter.

OWNERSHIP OF LAND

The whole of England belonged to the King by right of conquest and all who held land held it in his gift, whether they were Normans, other Frenchmen or Englishmen who had redeemed their possessions by submitting to him. The Domesday Book is not explicit about the nature of tenures in 1086 but it is known that the men under whose names the estates are listed were almost all holders of feudal honours and they owed, in return for their lands, a fixed quota of fully armed and equipped knights. In some cases land could be sub-let to others.

PEOPLE

Although many members of the English aristocracy lost, variously, their lives in battle, their property and their rights, they did have options: they could submit to William in return for favours. The Norman elite, who took over, became extremely rich, to the point where they could do virtually as they wished but it was also in their interests to avoid setting the local populace entirely against them. There was therefore some kind of balance but nevertheless English buildings were demolished and rebuilt over time. Norman architecture appeared where Anglo Saxon churches, large and small, once stood. At least four, and probably all, of the six churches in the Blewbury Hundred were so treated. Language, literature and records were destroyed or degraded to further subjugate the English people.

Beneath the level of the aristocracy, the population probably worked very much as before, albeit under greater duress and for much less personal return. The main workforce according to The Domesday Book consisted of villans, cottars and slaves. This was a simplification as "villans" included free men and not all slaves lived in total servility. The villans, especially if they held land, were better off than the others. Both cottars and villans can be thought of as the heads of households, each representing a family. Slaves on the other hand, if counted at all, were counted as individuals. Slavery was an Anglo Saxon tradition and the words slave and serf are synonymous. Slave ownership was an integral part of the system and although slaves had few rights themselves, their owners were responsible for them and their actions. Anyone killing or harming a slave had to compensate the slave's owner, not the slave. Killing your own slave brought disapproval from the church but otherwise went unpunished. Slavery could befall a person or family in a number of ways. The most common was as a penalty for crime but as a last resort, to avoid starvation, a person could sell himself and his family into slavery. The children of slaves were also slaves. A person could be bought out of slavery by anyone so-minded or the lord could grant him or her freedom. Slave ownership gradually died out under Norman and Early English rule with slaves being given land and rights similar to other workers.

Money

The coinage unit was the penny. The penny was the only coin struck; it was silver and about 20mm in diameter. Simply cutting pennies in half and in quarters made halfpennies and farthings. Higher units were not represented by coins either but were: the shilling (twelve pence) and the pound (twenty shillings or a pound of silver). Large payments were made by weight of coin or ingots of silver. The huge demand for coins was met by seventy mints in William's reign; the nearest to Blewbury was in Wallingford. The late Anglo-Saxon punishment for convicted counterfeiters and fraudsters was the amputation of hands.

Terms Used in the Survey

The "Hide" was the standard unit for assessment of tax; notionally the amount of land that would support a household, it is normally taken to be about 120 acres. A "Virgate" was a quarter of a hide. The familiar term "acre" was used as a measure of length as well as area in mediaeval times. As an area of land it was regarded as a field 66 by 660 feet. As a length it was the breadth of an acre, 66 feet or one furlong; the distance that a team of oxen could plough before stopping to rest and turn. The term "Meadow" was used to describe land bordering streams and liable to flood. It was abundant in an area such as this with its close network of streams. It was used for hay and for grazing working animals and sheep. A different "acre", now of unknown size, was used to quantify this land. "Mills" were all water driven; windmills did not appear in England till a century later. The word "Demesne" meant land whose produce was devoted to the lord rather

Village	Hides		Villans	Cottars	Slaves	Value	
	Pre 1066	1086				Pre 1066	1086
Blewbury	3.75	3.25	24	62	0	52	61
Harwell	26	15.5	30	17	9	29	37
East Hagbourne	15	11.7	18	16	6	15	18
West Hagbourne	9	6.5	14	10	4	13	13
South Moreton	10	5	7	8	6	12	13
Upton	10	5	16	7	7	13	13
Aston Tirrold	20	7	17	3	9	18	12
Aston Upthorpe	10	6.5	10	12	3	10	12
North Moreton	10	10	14	8	3	10	12
Willington	8	4.25	10	2	9	6	9
Fulscot	3	1	4	5	0	2	4
Total	124.75	75.75	164	150	56	180	204

Blewbury Hundred at a Glance. NB Value in £

than to his tenants. The initials "TRE" (Latin Tempore Regis Edwardi) is the abbreviation indicating the position 'in the time of King Edward', i.e. before the Conquest in 1066.

THE BLEWBURY HUNDRED

The Blewbury Hundred at the time of Domesday contained eleven villages in a rough circle of about a hundred square kilometres. All but Willington and Fulscot can be seen on the map today and are thriving villages. Beautiful Fulscot Manor is all that remains of Fulscot although there are tantalising rumours and some possible evidence on the ground of a deserted village and an earlier manor. It is possible that enclosure awards were responsible for the demise of the village. Willington has a different story. The Latin "Wibaldintone" in The Domesday Book, has been shown by Lingham [3] to be the 1086 name for modern Didcot. The transition from Wibaldintone to Dudecote occurred in the 12th century. The names Willington and Wibaldintone are both used in the references but refer to the same place. It is noted in the Domesday Book that the King's servants in Wallingford "...did service with horses or by water..." to Blewbury and other places.

Modern Name	Domesday Latin Name	Meadow Acres	Ploughs	Churches	Mills	Value 1086
Blewbury	Blitberie	26	36	1	4	61
Harwell	Harvvelle	45	24	1 chapel	1	37
East Hagbourne	Hacheborne	30	24		1	18
West Hagbourne	Hacheborne	24	13		1	13
South Moreton	Mortvne	80	9.5	1	1	13
Upton	Optone	30	17			13
Aston Tirrold	Estone	60	17			12
Aston Upthorpe	Estone	41	14	1		12
North Moreton	Mortvne	0	15	1	1	12
Didcot	Wibalditone	40	16	1		9
Fulscot Manor	Follesscote	30	4			4
Total		406	189.5	6	9	204

The tables above compare the villages before and after the conquest, ordered according to their 1086 value. Blewbury, Harwell and the Hagbournes were clearly seen as the most valuable. The relatively large number of ploughs and mills suggests that these were the productive, arable zones; and the larger population supports this suggestion. The general increase in perceived value after the conquest is in stark contradiction to the known conditions at the time.

PETER COCKRELL

Blewbury Hundred at a Glance. NB The Size of an "acre" of meadow is not now known.

ACKNOWLEDGEMENTS
THE HEADMASTER OF DRAGON SCHOOL OXFORD VERY KINDLY GAVE PERMISSION TO USE IMAGES FROM THE REPLICA OF DOMESDAY BOOK CREATED BY ALECTO HISTORICAL EDITIONS. THE PARTICULAR HELP OF GAY STURT OF DRAGON SCHOOL IS ALSO GRATEFULLY ACKNOWLEDGED, AS IS THAT OF HENRIETTA PEARSON OF ALECTO HISTORICAL EDITIONS.
THE DETAIL FROM THE VICTORIAN REPLICA OF THE BAYEUX TAPESTRY IN THIS ARTICLE IS COPYRIGHT READING MUSEUM SERVICE (READING BOROUGH COUNCIL). ALL RIGHTS RESERVED.

REFERENCES.
1. DOMESDAY BOOK – TRANSLATION AND STUDIES. ALECTO HISTORICAL EDITIONS. WWW.DOMESDAYBOOK.COM
2. DOMESDAY. A SEARCH FOR THE ROOTS OF ENGLAND. MICHAEL WOOD. BBC PUBLICATION 1986
3. THE LONG YEARS OF OBSCURITY – A HISTORY OF DIDCOT. VOLUME 1 TO 1841. 2ND EDITION. B.F.LINGHAM
4. DOMESDAY BOOK, BERKSHIRE. GENERAL EDITOR JOHN MORRIS, PHILLIMORE 1979
5. ANGLO-SAXON OXFORDSHIRE. JOHN BLAIR.
6. AN INTERESTING WEBSITE IS AT WWW.REGIA.ORG

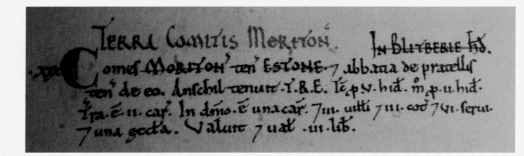

THE DOMESDAY BOOK

The Domesday Book was written in Latin in less than a year by one man. This is one of the seventeen entries involving the Blewbury Hundred with the English translation below. The numeral is the Count of Mortain's number in a list of sixty-five landholders in Berkshire, King William being number one. Robert, the Count of Mortain, was King William's half brother.

The Land of the Count of Mortain. In Blewbury Hundred.
19 The Count of MORTAIN holds ASTON TIRROLD, and the Abbey
of Preaux holds it of him. Eskil held it TRE. [It was] then [assessed] at
5 hides; now at 2 hides. There is land for 2 ploughs. In demesne is
1 plough; and 3 villans and 3 cottars and 6 slaves, and a church. It was
and is worth £3.

The book itself was constructed of parchment made from the, very carefully selected and prepared, skins of around two hundred sheep. Each was page was roughly 365mm by 255mm as thin as the paper of this book and carefully ruled to give two columns per page. Main headings were written with rich, red, vermillion ink made from mercury and sulphur and sub-headings were scored through with the same ink. The black ink was a solution containing galls, gum arabic, and iron salts. Over the centuries this has turned to various shades of brown. The plain lettering is about 2mm high.

FROM DOMESDAY TILL TODAY:
BLEWBURY'S THOUSAND YEARS FROM 1000 TO 2000AD

Stand on Blewburton Hill now and look around and you will see fields of crops and animals on the hill. Look further afield and you will see the villages of Blewbury and Aston nearby, with Upton, Didcot, Wallingford in the distance. From the time when invasions by Danes ceased and the water levels possibly decreased on the plain, people have chosen to live lower down from the Hill, nearer to water and with better protection from the harsher weather on the higher ground. As far as we can tell, there has been no permanent habitation on the Blewbury side of the Hill or on the top since Saxon times.

During the past 1000 years the village has nestled in the shelter of the Downs, and Blewburton has only been used to grow crops and animals. In 1086, as recorded in the Domesday Book, there were sixty-two cottars (cottagers), twenty-four villeins (tied tenants of the King and other landowners) and four mills in the Blewbury Hundred. That probably means there were as many as 90 dwellings forming the village but no remnants of any buildings have been found on the hillside. The cob walls that are so typical of Blewbury probably mark the boundaries of the old fields and properties, and the fact that so many have remained is testament to the village's peaceful past. Other remains are the occasional sarsen stones which are listed in manorial records as being property boundaries. The village layout has

MARIAN WHITING

St Michael's Church Blewbury.
By far the oldest building in the village. Some of the local churches are more than a thousand years old.

(Above): the intriguing cob walls in Blewbury, probably originally marking the boundaries of old fields and properties. (Below): Sheep near a thatched cob wall, still serving its purpose, in Blewbury 2005.

been substantially determined by the farming done up to about 1920. Cottagers and tenant farmers had small dwellings and farmed a few acres around their homes. The yeomen lived in larger houses but still farmed land around their property, as for example the Fullers in Hall Barn, or the successive Lords of the prebendal manor at Parsonage. In the village there was a plentiful supply of water whereas on Blewburton or on the Downs water would have had to be carried a distance or drawn from deep wells.

John Rocque's map of 1761 (see Chapter 9) shows no buildings East of what is now called the Didcot Road apart from Sheencroft and later ordnance survey maps also show no buildings there. Study of the Court Rolls makes no mention of the area other than the occasional field references. Despite the somewhat turbulent history of the hill as a fort, it appears to have played no part in the later history of the village.

The farming was a mixture of arable and sheep and cattle, with, certainly in the 19th and 20th centuries quite a lot of fruit orchards, primarily cherries. There are numerous references in the Court Rolls of the village to people not having cleaned watercourses, or not repairing fences and gates, or not having supplied the bull at the right time. Even up to 1901 the majority of the inhabitants were directly connected with agriculture, and a further number with trades such as baking, basket making or milling. The trade of the blacksmith and wheelwright continued into the 20th century, with four blacksmiths and three wheelwrights listed in 1901. Blacksmiths worked in the village till the 1950s because of the number of racing stables actually in the village, quite apart from those existing on the Downs.

The enclosure awards of 1759 and 1805 established ownership of land which settled larger tracts of land into the hands of a smaller number of farmers. It is interesting to see at the same time how the families of the larger landowners intermarried and ultimately increased their ownership.

During this time little has

Two of the older cottages in Blewbury: "Blue Haze" (left) and "Healmwic" (below). Cottagers and tenant farmers had small dwellings and farmed a few acres near their cottages. The yeomen lived in larger houses but still farmed land around their property. Villages would have been noisy places with many animals.

disturbed the even tenor of life in Blewbury. There have been a couple of Court cases concerning property. No battles have been fought here and the Industrial Revolution affected the village only lightly. In fact the population changed very little from the time of Domesday when it was about 400 people to 1901 when it had grown to about 600, with minor fluctuations in between. We have, for example, no records as to how much the Black Death of 1348-50 affected Blewbury. Some villages elsewhere are recorded as having lost up to 80% of their population, but some as few as 19% [1]. Since the village continued to exist it seems likely to be nearer the lower figure. It may be that land ownership changed as a result, but only contemporary tax and land returns could tell us.

There was, allegedly, a brief and potentially dangerous incident during the Civil War when Royalists and Roundheads ate at the same house, Hall Barn, within hours of each other. At that time, there were serious and bloody conflicts all around, at Newbury, Oxford (the headquarters of Charles I) and at Wallingford where there was a long siege. In 1645 there was even a large meeting of ordinary Berkshire townspeople and villagers held near Compton when they prepared a petition seeking an end to the fighting. That proved as abortive as such petitions are even today. The Fullers of Hall Barn were able to take a pragmatic view of the visiting armies and took no public stance for either side, and we have no reason to believe that other farming communities could not do likewise. Just over a hundred years later when the then owner of Hall Barn died he left goods to the value of £1225, so the brush with warring factions had not, apparently, seriously affected their prosperity.

The first big change to life in the village started to occur when the Great Western Railway was built, and transport to and from Newbury and London, and further afield became easier. But these changes were as nothing to the changes in agriculture which started at almost the same time. The Allens in their article have described some of the changes, but none of these resulted in a change to the agricultural use of Blewburton Hill.

Another change, which did not affect the number of people in the village greatly but which had, and still has, a great influence on the inhabitants, was the influx of the artists and writers that took place in the late 19th century. Artists such as T.F.M. Sheard, and Trissie Pearse, and writers such as G.B. Stern and Marguerite Steen brought something of the outside world to a quiet Berkshire village, a tradition which has been carried on into the 21st century.

The other big change has taken place from about 1945. At that time the Atomic Energy Research Establishment at Harwell, known locally as the "Atomic", caused an influx of young people to the area and new housing had to be provided. Since then, with more people moving into the area for the businesses that have grown up the population has increased greatly and by 2001 was about 1650. The number of people connected with agriculture has become minute and the village has a large number of people who work not only outside the village, but also outside the county. Interestingly, that statistic may now be reversing, with more people working from home using the Internet.

Blewburton then, is now the quiet hill between Blewbury and the Astons with not even a ghost story connection. As far as we can tell, there have been no stories about ghosts of the earlier people in the fort or of any mysterious happenings there, all such stories being recounted in connection with village houses or the Chalk Pit and the Downs. The village schoolchildren used to be taken to the Hill for Nature walks in the 1920s and 30s, and it is still a good place for a quiet stroll, and a chance to look down on the peaceful villages below, with little to remind one of the occasionally violent past of the fort.

AUDREY LONG
CHAIR, BLEWBURY LOCAL HISTORY GROUP

REFERENCE
THE WORLD UPSIDE DOWN, BLACK DEATH IN ENGLAND BY J. BOLTON, ED. ORMROD AND LINDLEY 1996

NEIGHBOURS TO THE NORTH
A VIEW FROM CASTLE HILL AT LITTLE WITTENHAM

© BERNARD MATTIMORE

A view of Wittenham Clumps from the South. Castle Hill is on the right.

After the last Ice Age ended around 10,000 BC and the glaciers had melted, humans, who had not been able to survive the intense cold, returned to the area. At first these were summer visitors, hunters following the reindeer as they migrated north through the Goring Gap into the Upper Thames valley, later permanent settlers living in the deciduous forests and on the river banks, hunting the giant elk, the aurochs (wild cattle, much larger even than modern bulls), red deer, wild boar and the beaver.

As the land was covered in forest, the rivers would have been important routeways, and the Sinodun Hills would have been crucial landmarks. Struck flint tools have been found on Castle Hill, alongside the Thames opposite Burcot and on the gravels in Paradise Wood and southeast of Long Wittenham, perhaps indicating a favoured route from the river to the hilltop.

EARLY FARMERS

Around 4000 BC the first farmers arrived in our area, bringing from
the Continent sheep and domestic cattle, cereal cultivation and pottery.
They cleared trees, or used clearings formed by high winds and by
beavers, and their grazing animals stopped the forest from regrowing,
creating openings in the woodland. One such site, where a pit and a
spread of struck flint was found, was on the edge of the plateau at Hill
Farm, Little Wittenham, and another at Macknay south of Brightwell.
Arrowheads and other flint tools show that they visited neighbouring
Castle Hill for hunting.

The scale of settlement was small, however, and we believe
they still moved around a large territory. They were the first to
build monuments, such as the processional way with circles of huge
timbers, and cremation burials in rings of pits, across the river north of
Dorchester. Finally, around 2600 BC, the Big Rings, a pair of concentric
circles formed by massive deep ditches with a bank in between, was
dug there as a ceremonial meeting place.

With the arrival of metal, society changed. People who owned the
gleaming copper and bronze became powerful, and showed their status
with metal weapons and ornaments, special drinking vessels called
Beakers, fired red in imitation of metal, and even a new type of flint
arrowhead. Traces of honey have been found in some Beakers, perhaps
from mead, an alcoholic drink made from honey.

Powerful individuals were given single burial under round
barrows. A group of these barrows stood around Northfield Farm, on
the gravels north of Castle Hill. They have all now been ploughed flat,
but aerial photographs, taken when the crops are turning from green
to yellow, show the circles of their surrounding ditches. All along the
Thames, clusters of these barrows were emerging, indicating smaller
tribal groupings. Settlements were however still few and small. Pollen
from peats show that much of the area of gravel terraces was now open
grassland and that local people were probably mainly pastoralists.

By 1500 BC, competition for grazing resulted in the first division
of the land at Northfield Farm and at Appleford. Enclosures and fields
appear all along the Thames at roughly this time, probably not only
due to competition for resources, but to increased production of goods

to exchange for metal objects brought by boat from the Continent. These field systems were also used for cereal cultivation, as we know from the charred cereals found in them. Additionally a new type of cereal, spelt wheat, was grown, which could be sown in autumn.

THE ANCIENT SETTLEMENTS

For much of the Bronze Age, from 2000 BC to around 1200 BC, the climate was warmer than today, and what is now the floodplain remained dry. Subsequently the climate became wetter and cooler, shortening the growing season, and resulting in extensive flooding. Increased rainfall also caused erosion of the cleared and cultivated areas. After a century or two this led to the abandonment of settlement on the floodplain, and possibly of the enclosure system at Northfield Farm as well.

A ditched enclosure was dug on the top of Castle Hill. The spoil from the ditch was thrown up to form a bank on the inner side, and a new settlement appeared below the hill stretching west from the Castle Hill Car Park. This was the first village of Little Wittenham, and was to last for 1500 years.

Radiocarbon dates from the ditch, and a large decorated pot found in it, date the enclosure to between 1050 BC and 900 BC. Human bone within the ditch suggests that one of its uses was for burial. The enclosure would have commanded a good view of the river Thames below, and would have been visible from Blewburton Hill. It demonstrated local power and provided a defence against hostile attack. The discovery of a sword chape at Hill Farm shows that warriors were present on the hilltop. A human skeleton with a bronze arrowhead embedded in the spine, and a dented shield, pierced in several places, was found in the Thames just below Castle Hill, providing positive evidence of warfare.

The land was not entirely tamed either, a large wolf bone (dated between 900 and 800 BC) was found in the village below Castle Hill. Substantial ditches and banks, like one just east of Long Wittenham, and another at Allen's Pit north of Dorchester, protected some of the earliest settlements from both wild animals and men.

The village below Castle Hill expanded into the early Iron Age. In some areas curving drainage gullies surrounded round houses;

in others there were pits for storage of seed corn and other materials. Squares of four posts (interpreted as raised storehouses or granaries) and a midden, were also discovered. The midden remains nearly a metre deep in places, and was at least fifty metres across. The variety of finds in similar middens in Hampshire, and the chalk floors within them, has led to the suggestion that they were the results of offerings at communal gatherings and a focus for ceremonies.

View of the Hillfort ditch and outer bank at Castle Hill looking south-west across the site of the adjacent settlement.

The village stretched for more than half a mile, and was probably the largest community in the area. The separation of activities indicates a highly organised settlement. Other smaller hamlets are known at North Moreton and at Northfield Farm, suggesting a densely populated landscape.

THE HILLFORT

This community replaced the hilltop enclosure on Castle Hill with the much larger hillfort that still survives today. Inside the hillfort a large pit containing nearly 2,500 animal bones, many of them of young pigs and lambs, together with a mixture of large communal cooking pots and small, red-coated bowls or cups, suggests that feasting occurred here. The hillfort probably acted as a refuge and a meeting place for tribal gatherings, marriages and burials, fairs and markets. The skeleton of a raven, found in the pit, suggests that rituals and religious beliefs were also important in the construction and use of the hillfort.

Middle Iron Age burial of a man with a charred offering at his feet.

Later in the Iron Age, the hillfort ditches were carefully maintained, as the chalk that had collapsed in from the sides was periodically cleaned out and dumped on the outer edge, eventually creating a bank five metres high. From the fort at Blewburton Hill, the white chalk bank of Castle Hill hillfort must have been clearly visible across the valley. Within the hillfort pits were dug. Some were filled

with decorated pottery and animal bones, but seven of the fourteen excavated contained either complete or partial human burials.

At the end of the Iron Age, burial seems to have shifted to areas just outside the hillfort; later, in the Roman period, burials were concentrated just outside the northeast gateway to the fort, in the outer bank and in the hillfort ditch.

SETTLEMENT ACROSS THE RIVER

The Middle Iron Age (400-0 BC) village was apparently organised into family enclosures either side of a curving boundary. Each roundhouse had storage pits, indicating mixed farming. They grew spelt wheat and barley and kept cattle, sheep and pigs, as well as horses and dogs. Evidence for textile manufacture and other crafts such as iron smithing has also been discovered. Some houses had an attached annexe and there are still groups of four-post granaries. Traces of settlement at the end of the Iron Age have only been found at Hill Farm; it is possible that some of the community moved to the new valley fort across the river at Dyke Hills, between the rivers Thames and Thame.

Dyke Hills was soon superseded by the new, small, Roman town of Dorchester which was served by a network of roads. The main road ran south through Brightwell towards Streatley. West of this, local ditched trackways can be traced, from the air, as cropmarks for long distances. One ran east west, from a river-crossing heading straight for Dorchester, to Long Wittenham, and thence to Roman villas at Appleford. A spur ran north past Northfield Farm to another river-crossing heading for a villa at Burcot.

By the mid-2nd century AD there were four rectangular ditched enclosures across the former Iron Age village area below Castle Hill, two of which contained buildings in Roman style visible from Blewburton Hill. One, above the disused Iron Age midden, was approached by a trackway from the southwest, and contained a stone-walled building with painted wall plaster, tiled roof and at least one mosaic floor. A second enclosure has within it a spread of limestones, roof tiles, and a few large tesserae.

TIMES OF CHANGE

Castle Hill, no longer the centre of the territory, continued as a cemetery and by the 4th century AD there were burials within the hillfort as well as outside. Towards the very end of the Roman period, from 350-400 AD, the hillfort may have been occupied by a farmstead; large pits were dug into the chalk on the hilltop, and a great quantity of pottery, animal bones and an assortment of nails, metal fittings, window and vessel glass, coins and other objects were dumped behind the rampart. This suggests domestic occupation very close by; it may indicate that, with bandits in the countryside and raids from the Saxons becoming frequent, some of the community had felt it safer to take refuge and resettle within the prehistoric defences.

Saxon pottery has been found within Castle Hill and to the south and the west of Hill Farm, so presumably the Late Roman settlement continued in the 5th and 6th centuries AD. There were already several Saxon communities in the area, at Dorchester and Abingdon, before the middle of the 5th century AD. There are certainly Roman-style burials, (dated by radiocarbon) continuing to the 5th century AD, at some of the Roman cemeteries around Dorchester. So we may envisage a Saxon aristocracy in the area, ruling over a native British population that clung to some of its old ways.

Cropmarks seen just east of Long Wittenham have been interpreted as the timber halls of an important Saxon settlement, perhaps those of a local prince, and there are two pagan Saxon cemeteries known in the village. The centre of local power may therefore have shifted again during the 5th and 6th centuries; the Saxons had no traditions of Roman stone towns or villa buildings, and tended to prefer to establish their own villages on new sites close by.

When the village below Castle Hill was finally abandoned is not clear, but it was almost certainly during the Saxon period, and was probably due to the influence of Christianity. We know that the manor of Little Wittenham was established in the Saxon period, since it is recorded in Domesday Book. It is likely that a new church and village were founded near the river in the mid-Saxon period (between 700 and 900 AD) - in sight of the bishop's own church. For Dorchester at this time, was the centre of a bishopric stretching from the Thames to Lincoln.

At this stage the church was not set within the ancient hillfort, perhaps because the pagan echoes of Castle Hill were too strong – Christianity was now taking over from the ancient gods. The success of the new village site owed much to the relocation of the cemetery, now alongside the church and not, as at Blewburton, located within the ancient hillfort. The greater ease of obtaining water must also have been an important factor.

Castle Hill now stood abandoned, and woodland apparently reappeared on part of the hilltop. Beech trees were growing there by the 12th century, when a small settlement was re-established, as is shown by pits containing Wallingford Ware, woodworking tools and charred thatch. By the late medieval period the hilltop was cleared, as we know from Leland who recorded waving corn there in 1560. The Wittenham clumps were planted in the mid-18th century by the lord of the manor, but around them arable cultivation continued. It was not until the later 19th century that settlement returned to the plateau below the hills, with Hill Farm and another small farm next to the Castle Hill Car Park. Both farms became redundant in the 20th century, though Hill Farm has found a new use as the offices of the Northmoor Trust, which now owns and manages the hilltops and the Little Wittenham Nature Reserve.

TIM ALLEN
OXFORD ARCHAEOLOGY

ACKNOWLEDGEMENTS
PERMISSION FROM THE NORTHMOOR TRUST AND THE HERITAGE LOTTERY INITIATIVE TO USE INFORMATION FROM THE RECENT EXCAVATIONS AT CASTLE HILL AND HILL FARM IS GRATEFULLY ACKNOWLEDGED, AS IS THE COLLABORATION OF OXFORD ARCHAEOLOGY.

LOCAL PLACE NAMES

When we hear in speech the names of the villages and towns around Blewburton Hill, we are hearing an echo of a language that was spoken in houses, on lanes and in markets before the time of King Alfred 1,200 years ago. The names of most places in southern England were created by the Anglo-Saxons, long before the Norman Conquest. In what was largely an illiterate society, the names carried crucial information about location, topography, function and ownership. Villages as we know them had not yet formed. Rather the names referred mainly to homesteads, farms or small settlements of a few, probably related families. The language was Germanic in origin and is known as Old English (abbreviated as OE).

Place-names are divided broadly into two types, one relating the place to a topographical feature, such as a hill, valley or stream and the other to settlement or land division. It is usually the word ending that contains this information, for instance the OE topographical word dun means "hill" or "down", while the OE words ham and tun mean "homestead", "village" or "estate". The first part of the name generally carries information that provides more specific information, often about

The village of Blewbury borrows its name from the bleo byrig component of the Old English name for Blewburton Hill, bleo byrig dun.

ownership or position relative to a significant place, and sometimes about usage or a natural feature.

Taking Blewburton Hill first, its name was formed from the OE bleo byrig dun, meaning: bleo "variegated", byrig "fort", and dun "hill". The "variegated" may relate to the light and dark variations caused by ploughing chalk-bearing soil. The village of Blewbury in turn borrows its name from the bleo byrig component of Blewburton Hill. The naming of a place relative to another is displayed with the Astons; the "Aston" component of both names is from the OE east "eastern" and tun. The name derives from its position relative to Blewbury or Blewburton Hill. The use of the suffixes is a later addition to distinguish the two holdings: Aston Tirrold by the family name of the landowner in the 12th Century from the Latin "Nicholaus filius Turoldi de Estuna", and "Upthorpe" meaning "the outlying settlement on higher ground", i.e. relative to Aston Tirrold, from OE upp "higher" and throp "outlying settlement"

The villages that lie to the north of the Astons, South and North Moreton use the OE mor "moor" or "marsh" and tun. The two are distinguished, relative to each other, by the OE north "northern" and suth "southern". The village to the west of Blewbury, Upton takes its name from it position on higher ground relative to Blewbury or West Hagbourne, from OE upp "higher" and tun. Three kilometres to the north of Blewbury are East Hagbourne and West Hagbourne which take the common part of their name from the stream that flows through them, i.e. "Hacca's stream", from an OE personal name Hacca and burna, "stream". To the west of the Hagbournes, along the ancient track known as the Driftway, is Harwell, which takes its name from the OE wella meaning "spring", "well" or "stream". The word har means "grey" and may refer to the water, or a nearby hill named "hara" meaning "the grey one".

A common element, cot meaning "cottage", appears in the name of a settlement that has since disappeared, that is Fulscot between Didcot and North Moreton. Here the first part is from the OE Fugol, either as a personal name or meaning "bird", since many place-names refer to associations with animals or plants. Finally, the increasingly important town of Didcot takes its name from the dwelling of a particular person named Dudda, as "Dudda's cottage", with the OE cot. Interestingly, the letter "u" persisted in Didcot's name well into the 19th Century, when it appears on an Ordnance Survey map of 1883 as "Dudcote".

STAN HUGHES

BIBLIOGRAPHY
1. CAMERON, K. 1996. ENGLISH PLACE NAMES. LONDON.
2. GELLING, M. (1973-76). THE PLACE NAMES OF BERKSHIRE – PARTS I, II & III. CAMBRIDGE.
3. INSTITUTE FOR NAME STUDIES, WEBSITE: WWW.NOTTINGHAM.AC.UK/ENGLISH/INS
4. LINGHAM, B.F. 1978. THE LONG YEARS OF OBSCURITY: A HISTORY OF DIDCOT VOL 1 ~ TO 1841.

Appendix

English Translations of the Latin Domesday Book Entries
For the Blewbury Hundred 1086

BLEWBURY

THE COUNT of Evreux himself holds BLEWBURY. Beorhtweard held it TRE. [It was] then [assessed] at 2 hides; now at 1 virgate. There is land for 1 plough. There are 4 cottars, and a mill rendering 4s, and 10 acres of meadow. It was worth 40s; now 20s.

The king holds BLEWBURY in demesne. King Edward held it. Then, as now, [it was assessed at] 3 hides. There is land for 20 ploughs. In demesne are 4 ploughs; and 24 villans and 58 cottars with 15 ploughs, and there are 3 mills rendering 37s 6d, and 16 acres of meadow. TRE and afterwards it was worth £50; now £60. Of this manor William Beaufour holds the church with 5 virgates of land. Ælfric held it of King Edward. There are 3 cottars, and 10 acres of meadow. It is and was worth 100s.

HARWELL

ROGER D'IVRY holds HARWELL. Wulfric, a free man, held it TRE. [It was] then [assessed] at 6 hides; now at 3 hides. There is land for 5 ploughs. In demesne are 2 ploughs; and 7 villans and 7 cottars with 2 ploughs. There

are 2 slaves, and a chapel. It was worth £12; now £15.

The same Roger holds HARWELL of the fief of Earl William. Aki, a free man, held it TRE. [It was] then [assessed] at 5 hides; now at 2 1/2 hides. There is land for 4 ploughs. In demesne is 1 [plough]; and 5 villans and 5 cottars with 1 plough, and there are 3 slaves. It was worth £5; now £6.

The bishop himself holds HARWELL in demesne as of his bishopric. Bishop Stigand held it TRE. [It was] then [assessed] at 15 hides; now at 10 hides. There is land for 8 ploughs. In demesne are 2 ploughs; and 18 villans and 5 cottars with 6 ploughs. There are 4 slaves, and a mill rendering 30d, and 45 acres of meadow; and in Wallingford 3 closes rendering 15d. TRE, and afterwards, it was worth £12; now £16.

EAST HAGBOURNE

REGENBALD of Cirencester holds [East] HAGBOURNE of the king. He himself held it of King Edward. There are 15 hides; but then, as now, it was assessed at 12 hides less 1 virgate. There is land for 12 ploughs. In demesne are 2

ploughs; and 18 villans and 16 cottars with 10 ploughs. There are 6 slaves, and a mill rendering 12s 6d, and 30 acres of meadow. It was worth £15; now £18.

WEST HAGBOURNE

WALTER FITZOTHER holds [West] HAGBOURNE. Alwine, a free man, held it. Then, as now, [there were] 10 hides, but it is assessed at 6 1/2 hides. There is land for 6 ploughs. In demesne are 2 ploughs; and 14 villans and 10 cottars with 5 ploughs. There are 4 slaves, and a mill rendering 12s, and 24 acres of meadow. Of this and Robert holds 1 hide of Walter, and there he has 1 plough with 1 cottar, and 4 acres of meadow. The whole, TRE and afterwards, was worth £13; and now £13.

SOUTH MORETON

WILLIAM LOVET holds [South] MORETON. Toti held it of King Edward. Then [it was assessed] at 5 hides; now at 2 1/2 hides. There is land for 4 ploughs. In demesne is 1 [plough]; and 3 villans and 4 cottars with 1 1/2 ploughs. There is a mill rendering 12s 6d, and 40 acres of meadow. It was and is worth £6, although it renders £7.

HUMPHREY Visdeloup holds [South] MORETON. Osmund, a free man, held it TRE. [It was] then [assessed] at 5 hides; now at 2 1/2 hides. There is land for 3 ploughs. In demesne are 2 ploughs]; and 4 villans and 4 cottars with 1 plough. There is a church, and 6 slaves, and 40 acres of meadow. It is and was worth £6.

UPTON

The same Turstin holds UPTON. Beorhtric, a free man, held it. [It was] then [assessed] at 10 hides; now at 5 hides. There is land for 9 ploughs. In demesne are 2 [ploughs]; and 16 villans and 7 cottars with 6 ploughs. There are 7 slaves, and 30 acres of meadow. It is and was worth £13.

ASTON TIRROLD

The king holds ASTON TIRROLD in demesne. The wife of Lang held it of King Edward. [It was] then [assessed] at 15 hides; now at 5 hides. There is land for 7 ploughs. In demesne is 1 [plough]; and 14 villans with 7 ploughs, and there are 3 slaves, and 60 acres of meadow. TRE it was worth £15; and afterwards £12; now £9.

The Count of MORTAIN holds ASTON TIRROLD, and the Abbey of Preaux holds it of him. Eskil held it TRE. [It was] then [assessed] at 5 hides; now at 2 hides. There is land for 2 ploughs. In demesne

is 1 plough; and 3 villans and 3 cottars and 6 slaves, and a church. It was and is worth £3.

ASTON UPTHORPE

REGENBALD of Cirencester holds ASTON UPTHORPE. Æthelgifu, a certain free woman, held it TRE. Then there were 10 hides; but it was assessed at 6 1/2 hides then, as now. There is land for 7 ploughs. In demesne are 2 ploughs; and 10 villans and 12 cottars with 5 ploughs. There are 3 slaves, and 41 acres of meadow. It was worth £10; now £12.

NORTH MORETON

WILLIAM fitzCorbucion The same William holds [North] MORETON, and Ralph [holds] of him. A certain free man held it TRE. Then, as now, [it was assessed] at 10 hides. There is land for 7 ploughs. In demesne are 2 ploughs; and 14 villans and 8 cottars with 6 ploughs, and a mill rendering 12s 6d. There is a church, and 3 slaves, and in Wallingford 5 closes rendering 50d. It was worth £10; now £12.

DIDCOT (WILLINGTON)

HENRY holds WILLINGTON, and Nigel [holds] of him. Thorkil, a free man, held it of King Edward. There is land for 6 ploughs. [It was] then [assessed] at 8 hides; now at 4 hides and 1 virgate. There is a church, and 9 slaves, and 2 ploughs in demesne, and 10 villans and 2 cottars with 8 ploughs, and 40 acres of

meadow. It was worth £6; now £9.

FULSCOT

Roger fitzSeifrid holds FULSCOT of the king. Ludric, a certain free man, held it TRE. Then at 3 hides it was assessed at 1 hide [sic]; now the same. There is land for 2 ploughs. In demesne is 1 [plough]; and 4 villans and 5 cottars with 1 plough, and 30 acres of meadow. It was worth 40s; now £4.

IN THE BOROUGH OF WALLINGFORD KING EDWARD HAD 8 virgates of land, and in these were 276 closes

rendering £11 from rent, and they who dwelt there did service for the king with horses or by water as far as Blewbury, Reading, Sutton Courtenay [and] Benson [Oxon.], and to those who did this the reeve gave cash or kind not from the rent of the king but from his own.

ACKNOWLEDGEMENTS
THE above translations are reproduced from "DOMESDAY BOOK – TRANSLATION AND STUDIES". WITH PERMISSION FROM ALECTO HISTORICAL EDITIONS.